W9-BGX-323

Young Readers Edition

THE FISHES

F. D. Ommanney

and the Editors of TIME-LIFE BOOKS

TIME INCORPORATED, NEW YORK

ON THE COVER: Resident of a
Pacific Ocean reef, a brilliantly
colored wrasse cruises in search
of food. Its strong blue teeth are
used to crack open shellfish.

LIFE WORLD LIBRARY

LIFE NATURE LIBRARY

TIME READING PROGRAM

THE LIFE HISTORY OF THE UNITED STATES

LIFE SCIENCE LIBRARY

GREAT AGES OF MAN

TIME-LIFE LIBRARY OF ART

TIME-LIFE LIBRARY OF AMERICA

FOODS OF THE WORLD

THIS FABULOUS CENTURY

LIFE LIBRARY OF PHOTOGRAPHY

© 1967, 1970 Time Inc. All rights reserved.
Published simultaneously in Canada.
Library of Congress catalogue card number 67-31538.

Contents

Introduction

A fascinating glimpse into the extraordinary world of fishes is provided by this fact-filled and beautifully illustrated volume. The fishes outdo the land-living back-boned animals in many ways. They are much older as a group and, in fact, were the ancestors of all land animals. Despite this age they are still evolving; there are many more species of fishes than of back-boned land animals, and new kinds are being discovered all the time.

Fishes live in a fantastic variety of habitats, from the darkest depths of the ocean to the boundless surface of the open sea. They are found from the tropics to the poles, in muddy bays and rushing rivers—even in caves, where blind and colorless fish live as deep as a thousand feet underground. Some fishes spend part of their lives out of the water and will drown if kept submerged; some hibernate in mud cocoons when their pools dry up, while others travel overland to find new watery homes. Wherever they live, fishes have become marvelously adapted to the different environments of which they are a part. No wonder they are so many and so diverse.

For man, fishes not only provide a major source of sport and recreation, they also provide by far the greatest wildlife crop. In a world where population is growing so rapidly that it is running out of nourishing animal protein, the lives of millions of people may depend on the proper harvesting of fish as food.

CARL L. HUBBS
Professor of Biology, Emeritus
Scripps Institution of Oceanography
University of California, San Diego

1
The Busy World beneath the Surface

TWO TROUT hover next to small boulders in a
Montana stream as a fawn wades into the water
without noticing them. The fish and fawn are
physically close, but their worlds are far apart. The
fish's realm is water, an environment that affects
all it does, including how it breathes and moves.

The waters that cover about 75 per cent of
our world teem with so many swimming,
wriggling, crawling and floating animals that
we can scarcely realize how immense are
their numbers. Fishes swarm this planet in
millions upon millions, breeding, growing,
living, dying in everything from puddles
and ponds to the great oceans. Not even the
seemingly endless variety of insects can
match the diversity in size and shape displayed by the fishes, who range from tiny
animals to monsters 50 feet long. And of
all the earth's vertebrate creatures—creatures with backbones—they are the oldest.
Fishes thrived in the water for long ages before the first of them ventured out of it onto
the land to begin the long, slow evolution-
ary process that gave rise to the mammals
and finally to man. In a sense, this makes
men and fishes cousins—even if very distant ones.

However, until comparatively recent times
man has known very little about the lives of
his "relatives," largely because the water in
which they live is so different from man's
airy surroundings. Beneath the vast waters,
the fishes' evolution and way of life far back

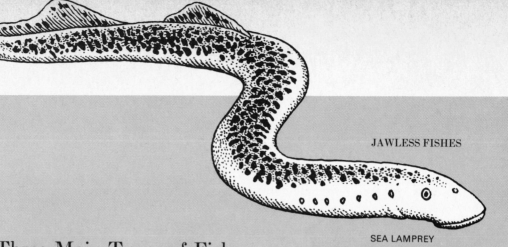

JAWLESS FISHES

SEA LAMPREY

The Three Main Types of Fish

The living fishes are grouped in three general types or classes. The most primitive class consists of the jawless fishes, like the sea lamprey shown above. Another class has the jaw-breaking name of cartilaginous fishes—fishes with skeletons made of cartilage rather than bone; the deep water chimaera *(bottom)* as well as sharks, skates and rays are of this type. The bony fishes, whose skeletons are made of bone, constitute the third class. These include almost all of the most advanced and familiar fishes, such as the Atlantic sturgeon *(below)*.

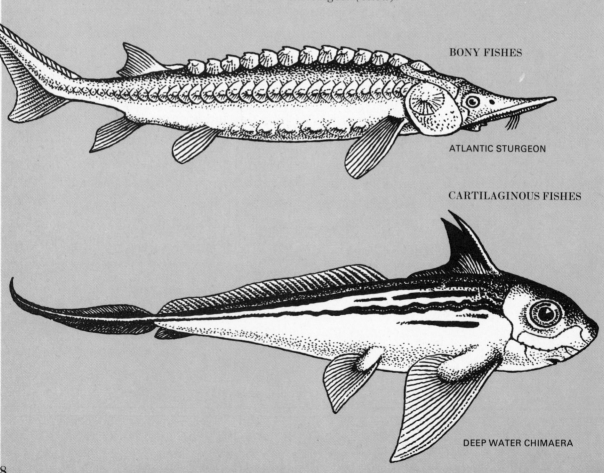

BONY FISHES

ATLANTIC STURGEON

CARTILAGINOUS FISHES

DEEP WATER CHIMAERA

in prehistory took a course quite different from that of man.

Making use of every nook and niche of their vast domain, fishes have developed not only in unimaginable numbers but also in bewildering and bizarre shapes. Some fishes have survived almost unchanged through hundreds of millions of years of evolution: these include the sharks and rays, the lampreys, the hagfishes, the bichirs of Africa, the lungfishes and the Mississippi paddlefish. There are fishes that breathe air as well as water, others that walk or fly as well as swim. There are fishes that bear live young, and others that lay eggs. There are round fishes, flat fishes, tube-shaped fishes; there are fishes that cannot lead an independent existence of their own; there are fishes that migrate thousands of miles and others that spend their entire lives in the same hole. There are at least 20,000 species of fish that we recognize today—and perhaps more not yet even discovered.

How did such an astonishing array of fishes come into being? What is the history of fish on earth? No one is sure, but certain clues have been found in fossil remains—those imprints of prehistoric animals and plants found in ancient layers of rock.

Six hundred million years ago, the date of the earliest fossil record uncovered thus far, this planet was already about four billion years old. Looking back across such a great length of time, the changes worked by evolution can be seen fairly clearly. As in a slow-speed movie of a flower's growth from seedling to full bloom, we can picture for ourselves the growth of life from a single-celled micro-organism drifting in the sea to the complex structure of a fish we know today. Time was the key factor in the process of evolution—time for life to grow, branch out, explore, adapt itself, develop new forms and modifications, discard and refine others. Time there was aplenty. In making a slow-speed movie that re-created the evolution of a fish we could not take a different picture more often than once every 100,000 years if we wanted to show the small changes that occurred during the long, slow process of natural selection.

Six hundred million years ago evolution took place entirely in the sea. Except for a few plants exposed to the air twice daily on the tidal flats where they grew, no living things dwelled on land. The oceans that lapped the bare land were far different from the submarine world we know today. They were wide, warm and shallow, and all life that they contained was on or near the bottom. There were no fishes as we know them, but trilobites (ancestors of today's horseshoe crabs), sponges, snails, jellyfishes, worms and other creatures teemed in the sunlit waters. And somewhere, either in the oceans or in some fresh-water pond or stream of that far-off day, was a creature that would eventually give rise to the fishes and, through them, in time, to the amphibians, reptiles, mammals and man himself.

9

We can only guess at what this creature looked like, how it functioned and lived, for if it left a fossil record, that record disappeared long ago, crumbled and eroded away.

Certainly it did not look much like the fish we know. It probably had no real head, brain or advanced sense organs, jaws or teeth or pairs of fins. Most likely, its body was cylindrical, with simple digestive organs, a nerve cord running its full length and below that a sort of stiffening, supporting rod, called a notochord, which was its only skeleton. The notochord, the forerunner of the backbone, explains the name chordates given to all animals having this feature or its later development, the spinal or vertebral column. The first chordate fish, scientists believe, breathed and fed through organs called internal gills and were confined to shallow water through which they moved by wriggling. But we do not know what gave rise to fishlike animals, for there is a gap of perhaps 100 million years, which we will probably never be able to fill. And in those millions of years some very significant events must have taken place which shaped the future of fishes for all time. For by the time that the fossil record becomes more definite, fish developed jaws, paired fins, a brain and a basic supporting structure. On some fish this structure was outside armor, on others it was an internal skeleton; both forms enabled them to move quickly, smoothly and easily, rather than in jerks like tadpoles.

The underwater picture was also changing greatly. The seas had advanced and receded from the continents several times. Mountain ranges had pushed up and eroded, deserts had formed and been drowned. Land plants had appeared and were by now plentiful. In the sea, corals spread, building reefs where sea lilies waved in the currents. Shellfish were numerous, and many new forms of sponges were abundant. But the biggest change in scene was in the water itself, for now there were fishes in many shapes, swimming through a world that had so long been empty of living things.

The fossil record the fishes left behind is so extensive that this period is sometimes called the Age of Fishes. From the fossils it is clear that fishes were constantly adapting to the many opportunities they had to spread out and to invade every part of their environment. They did not become more complicated as they evolved; if anything, the tendency was for them to become more simple. The useful additions to their basic structure that developed, such as jaws and paired fins, were new tools to make better use of their surroundings.

When fishes started swimming actively, rather than just wiggling through the water, some sort of balancing mechanism became necessary to prevent pitching and rolling. The pairs of pectoral and pelvic fins that thrust out from the sides of the body were the answer to this problem. With the addition of these fins came a greatly improved swimming skill.

(*Text continued on page 14*)

The Fresh-Water Fishes

ON THE FOLLOWING PAGES

Whether the earliest fishes lived in the sea or in fresh water is still a matter of discussion among scientists. But when fish developed jaws and paired fins, they spread to waters all over the world. On the following two pages is a painting showing some typical fish that live in fresh water; they are identified in the key at right and below. Fresh-water fish are limited in the kinds of places where they can roam; most cannot enter salt water. Since their environment is narrower, fresh-water fish are not as abundant as saltwater fish, nor are there as many different types.

1 Brook trout
2 Stickleback
3 White sucker
4 Golden shiner
5 Lamprey
6 Chain pickerel
7 Bluegill sunfish
8 Black-nosed dace
9 Small-mouth bass
10 Black crappie
11 Perch
12 Brown bullhead
13 Yellow bullhead

14 Lake trout
15 White crappie
16 Eel
17 Burbot
18 Carp
19 Salmon
20 Great northern pike
21 Winter flounder
22 Young bluefish
23 Brown trout
24 Shad
25 Striped bass

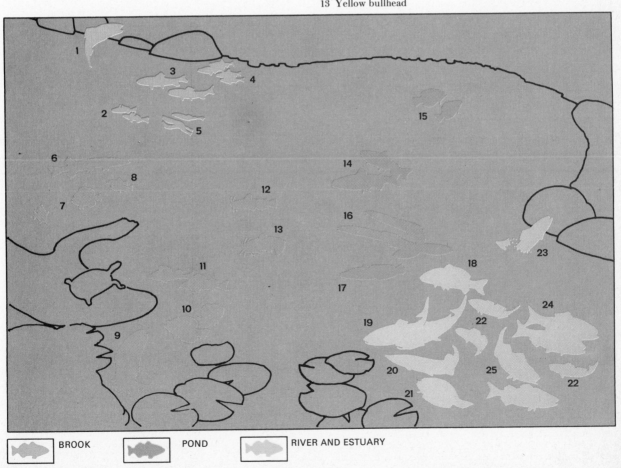

BROOK   POND   RIVER AND ESTUARY

For all the enormous diversity that developed during the Age of Fishes, there are certain things common to all fishes, forced upon them by the conditions of the medium in which they live—water.

Water has given fishes their general shape, their way of breathing, their method of moving, of feeding, of reproducing their own kind. Water has even given them, as we shall see, a sixth sense that no other animal has. The nature of the world of water—its shallows and depths, its temperatures and currents, the animal and vegetable life that exist in it—has offered fishes all kinds of chances for specialization. Life in the water is responsible for their basic coloration; in the darkest depths, where no light ever goes, some fishes have even developed their own special lighting systems, while others have actually become blind.

Almost without exception, fishes are to be found wherever there is permanent water, from mountain streams to the depths of the oceans and even in underground rivers. Few natural bodies of water are so hot, so cold, so salty that fish cannot live in them. There are even some fishes that have adapted themselves to living in pools that dry up for considerable periods.

The various colors of fishes are directly connected with the areas in which they live. With few exceptions, fishes are colored according to a basic general plan—dark above and light below. But those that live close to the surface tend to have a bluish or greenish cast; those that live near or on the bottom are usually brown on back and sides; while those that live in the depths of the sea beyond the zone of light are almost always either black or silvery.

Like other animals, fishes eat a variety of food, alive and dead, plant and animal. Some eat only plants, many are flesh-eaters; some flesh-eaters feed only on the plant-eaters; other flesh-eaters eat only flesh-eaters. There are scavengers that eat only dead matter, and a good many fishes that eat both plant and animal foods. A large number of fishes live on plankton, the tiny organisms in the surface layers of the sea. Finally, there are fishes that suck the body fluids of other fishes.

On the other hand, greater numbers of fish feed on plankton—a crop that the oceans have in quantity—than on any other food. Plankton consist of scores of both plants and animals—many of them single-celled and microscopic in size, drifting about the water in clouds. It has been calculated that over an entire year the North Atlantic yields about one ton of plankton per acre (the average yield of hay in a fertile field is a little more than one and a half tons). Nonetheless, the total amount of living plants produced annually by all the world's oceans exceeds that produced on land, since the oceans constitute such a large proportion of the earth's surface.

Each year the waters of the world produce

(*Text continued on page 18*)

ON THE FOLLOWING PAGES

The Salt-Water Fishes

The painting on the following two pages shows some
typical fish found in salt water at various depths;
they are identified in the key at right and below.
Salt-water fish have entire seas to swim in, yet most
live in the shallower waters near the shore, above the
Continental shelves and slopes, the area where the
shelves trail away into deep-water valleys. Since
competition is less sharp in the deep water, many
primitive fish species, like the black swallower, have
lived there for hundreds of thousands of years.

1	Hammerhead shark	17	Tuna
2	Flyingfish	18	Pollack
3	Manta	19	Cod
4	Mummichog	20	Haddock
5	Tidewater silverside	21	Flounder
6	Scup	22	Sea robin
7	Sculpin	23	Swordfish
8	Menhaden	24	Goosefish
9	Tautog	25	Skate
10	Bluefish	26	Ocean pout
11	Halibut	27	Chimaera
12	Weakfish	28	Photostomias quernei
13	Dolphin	29	Hatchetfish
14	Herring	30	Lanternfish
15	Puffer	31	Black swallower
16	Dogfish		

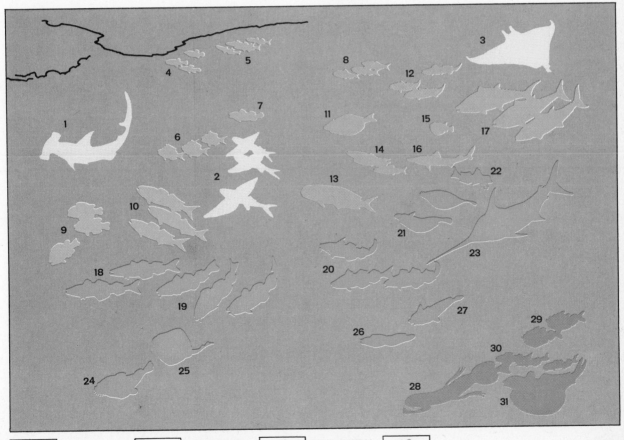

 SURFACE   CONTINENTAL SHELF   CONTINENTAL SLOPE   DEEP SEA

15

an estimated 500 billion tons of plant plankton. Much of this production is eaten by animal plankton, and the plankton-feeding fishes in turn eat the animal plankton along with the plant plankton. Since the plankton drift about the oceans on or near the surface, these fishes are for the most part surface dwellers that travel in large schools. They include such species as the herring, mackerel, menhaden, capelin and many others. There are nonschooling fishes among them too, one of the most notable being the largest of all living fishes, the whale shark, which grows up to 50 feet long. Among river fishes the Mississippi paddlefish is a plankton-feeder.

To obtain the tiny plankton from water, fishes need a strainer of some sort, and this they have developed in the form of close-set structures called gill rakers arranged in rows as in a comb. Most of the plankton-feeders obtain their food by swimming along with their mouths open, straining quantities of water through their gills. The plankton collects on the gill rakers as the water streams out through the gill slits.

Since the plankton-feeders are probably the most abundant of all fishes and are generally fairly small in size, they are the main food source for the large and ferocious flesh-eating predators such as the bluefish, thresher shark, and giant tuna.

Some of the most important commercial fishes of the sea are flesh-eaters, as are the

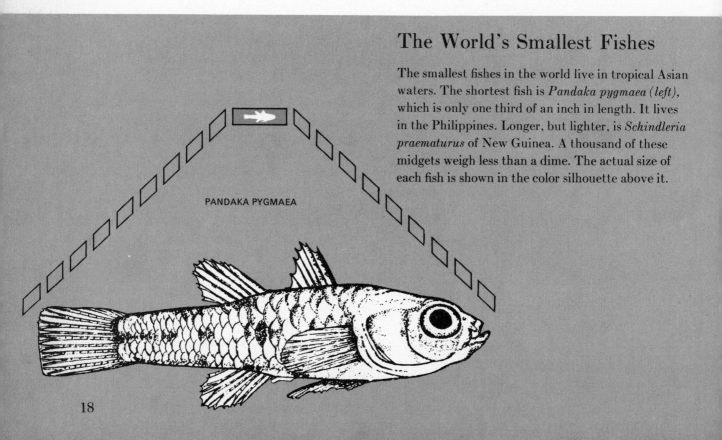

The World's Smallest Fishes

The smallest fishes in the world live in tropical Asian waters. The shortest fish is *Pandaka pygmaea (left)*, which is only one third of an inch in length. It lives in the Philippines. Longer, but lighter, is *Schindleria praematurus* of New Guinea. A thousand of these midgets weigh less than a dime. The actual size of each fish is shown in the color silhouette above it.

PANDAKA PYGMAEA

18

great sporting species. The Atlantic tarpon, which may reach a length of eight feet and weigh as much as 340 pounds, is one of the most spectacular fighters of all. The teeth of some predatory fishes are frightening tools. Piranhas, for example, have teeth with cutting edges sharp as razors. The white shark grows teeth with edges serrated like steak knives, and still other fishes have teeth like needles that serve mainly to secure a firm grip on their prey. A few species of fish, like the wolf fish of the North Atlantic, the Port Jackson shark and the eagle ray, have developed massive crushing teeth to cope with the hard shells of mollusks, such as clams and oysters.

Naturally, fishes tend to live where their food is most abundant. Beyond that, however, what prevents fishes from ranging any part of the great oceans in which most of them live? What, if anything, fences them in? What keeps them at "home"?

The fact is that there are quite definite barriers to the spread of animals in water. Among these, temperature is one of the most obvious and important. Compared to the variations we know on the land, the range of temperature in any sizable body of water is small. In any given area of ocean, it generally varies no more than about 25° Fahrenheit. The hottest seas in the world are the Red Sea and the Persian Gulf, where temperatures of 86° F. occur. The coldest are in the Arctic and Antarctic, where a temperature

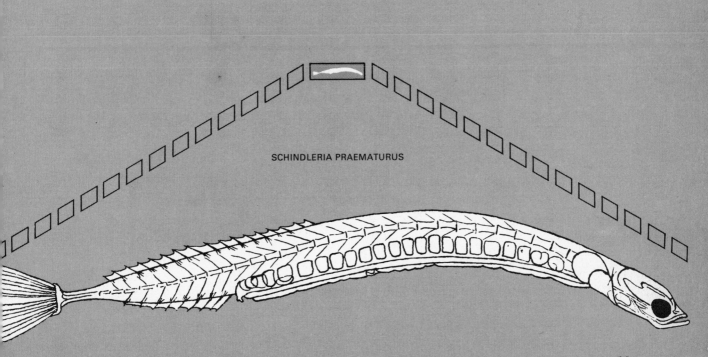

SCHINDLERIA PRAEMATURUS

19

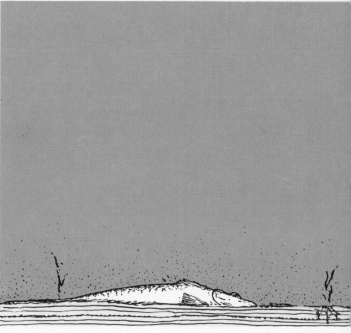

as low as 28°F., four degrees below the freezing point of fresh water, is not unusual. By comparison, extremes of temperature on land may range all the way from −126°F., on the Antarctic continent, to 136°F. in the North African Sahara.

Except in high latitudes or cold weather, the temperature decreases with the depth below the surface, where the water is always warmest—but it does not drop in even stages. In any sizable body of water there is usually a zone in mid-depth where the temperature falls rapidly in a relatively short distance. Below this zone the temperature changes little the year round. Smaller bodies of water naturally vary more widely in their seasonal temperatures than do the oceans, although very seldom does the water's temperature reach that of the surrounding air.

On the bottom, unless the lake or stream freezes solidly in winter, temperatures rarely fall below 39°F.

Fishes are present in water of every temperature from the tropics to the poles, but they are most abundant in the temperate latitudes where temperatures range between about 43°F. and 68°F. Most fishes can put up with a fluctuation of 12°F. to 15°F., if the change is not made too suddenly. Not surprisingly, fish eggs and young fish are more sensitive to these fluctuations than are adults, which may often be found living in areas that are either too warm or too cold for the eggs or the immature fish.

There is nothing fixed about the temperature zones of the seas; the zones may, and in fact occasionally do, shift drastically. Some-

times the changes that occur have a benefi-
cial effect, as far as man is concerned. Since
the early 1900s, for example, there has been
a general warming-up over the whole North
Atlantic, particularly near the Arctic Circle.
The result has been a marked increase in the
numbers of cod around Bear Island, Greenland and the north coast of Norway. British
and Russian trawlers were quick to take
advantage of this change.

There are other times, however, when
changes in the temperature may have terrible results for the fishes. In 1882 the important tilefish industry of southern New England was virtually wiped out by abrupt and
major water changes. It is generally believed
that strong gales, which swept that part of
the Atlantic repeatedly during the winter,
flooded the bottom with cold water. In any

How a Fish Fossil Is Formed

On the opposite page, prehistoric fish called Prisacaras
are shown swimming in a Wyoming lake about 50
million years ago. After one dies and falls to the
bottom (*next picture*), its body is covered with
sediment. Millions of years later the lake has dried up
and its bottom sediments have formed layers of
sandstone in which the fish is crushed (*above, left*).
Still later the sandstone is exposed by earth movements
and gradually worn away (*above*), uncovering the
fossil—an imprint of the body in the stone (*below*).

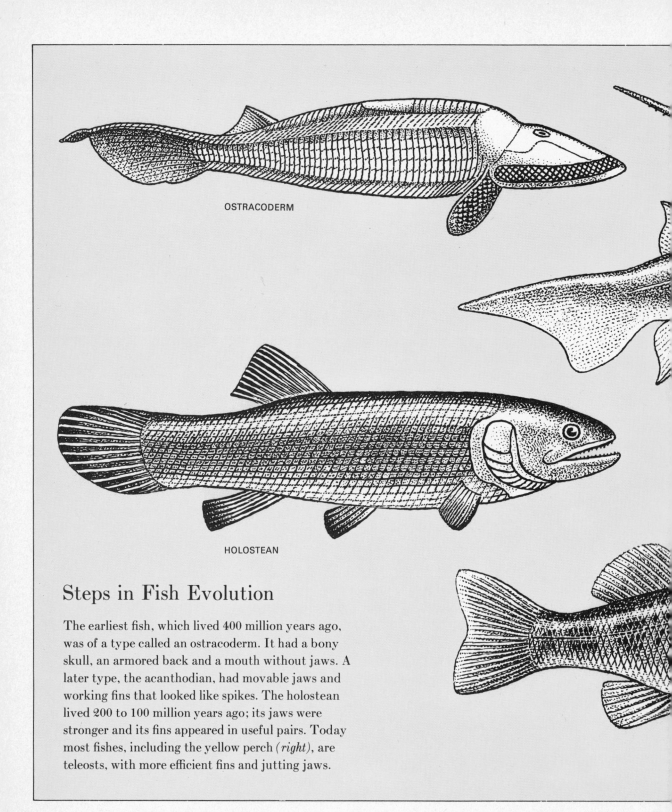

OSTRACODERM

HOLOSTEAN

Steps in Fish Evolution

The earliest fish, which lived 400 million years ago, was of a type called an ostracoderm. It had a bony skull, an armored back and a mouth without jaws. A later type, the acanthodian, had movable jaws and working fins that looked like spikes. The holostean lived 200 to 100 million years ago; its jaws were stronger and its fins appeared in useful pairs. Today most fishes, including the yellow perch (*right*), are teleosts, with more efficient fins and jutting jaws.

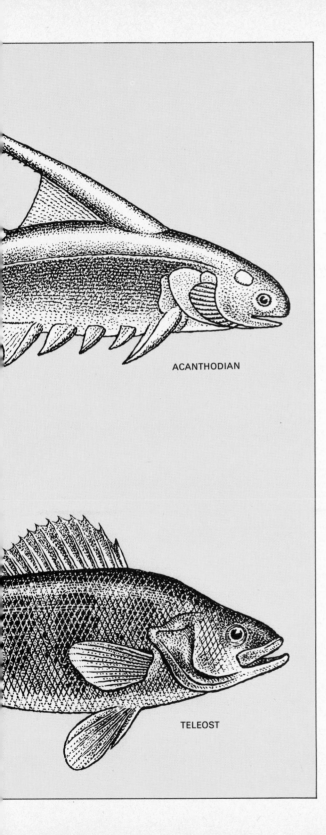

ACANTHODIAN

TELEOST

case, an estimated 1.5 billion dead tilefish were seen floating on the surface of the ocean, and the total destruction was such that the fishery could not be re-established for many years.

Off the coast of Peru catastrophes like this happen with some regularity, although they are not due to temperature changes alone but also to sudden shifts in the supply of food or the salt content of the water. The northward-flowing Humboldt, or Peruvian, Current off the west coast of South America is the chief supplier of fish food in this area. The extreme richness of this current is due to the surge of cold water, loaded with nutrients on which plankton feed, from the ocean bottom. This upwelling is produced largely by the action of the prevailing offshore winds, which drive the surface water away from the coast. Plankton thrive on this cold, rich water, and they in turn serve as rich food for fishes, particularly the anchoveta, which are so abundant that recently Peru has exported more than 4.5 million tons of anchoveta, ground into fish meal, in a single year. The Peruvian output has dominated the world market for this product.

There are years, however, when the winds diminish and then the surface water is not driven away from the coast. As a result the upwelling of cold water lessens and the surface layers warm up more than usual. With fewer nutrients to feed on, the plankton soon die. Millions of fishes that feed on plankton

(*Text continued on page 26*)

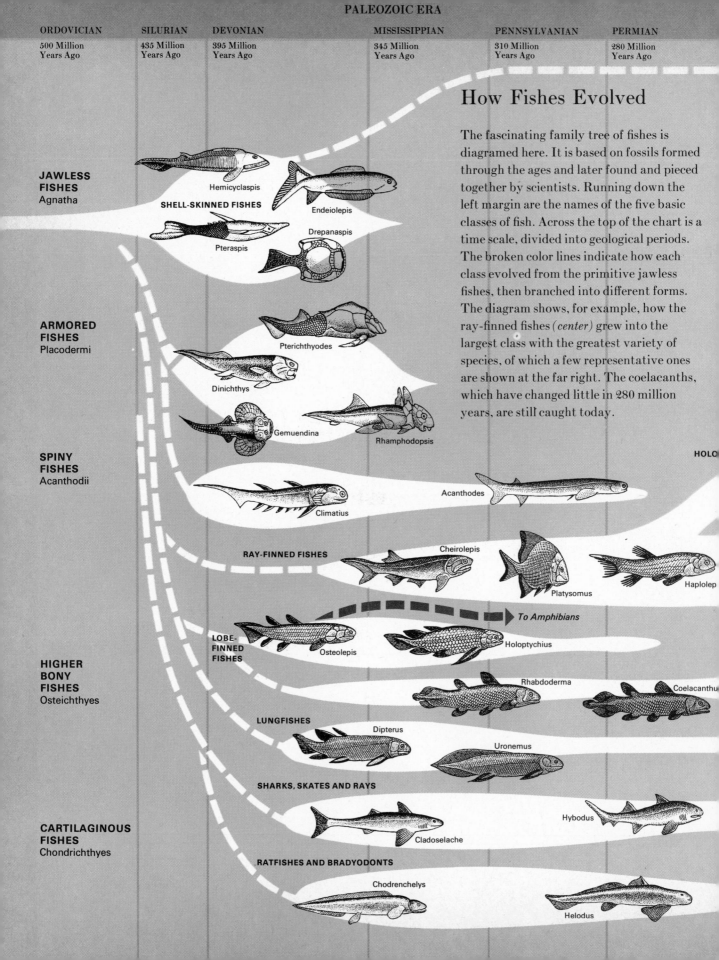

PALEOZOIC ERA

ORDOVICIAN	SILURIAN	DEVONIAN	MISSISSIPPIAN	PENNSYLVANIAN	PERMIAN
500 Million Years Ago	435 Million Years Ago	395 Million Years Ago	345 Million Years Ago	310 Million Years Ago	280 Million Years Ago

How Fishes Evolved

The fascinating family tree of fishes is diagramed here. It is based on fossils formed through the ages and later found and pieced together by scientists. Running down the left margin are the names of the five basic classes of fish. Across the top of the chart is a time scale, divided into geological periods. The broken color lines indicate how each class evolved from the primitive jawless fishes, then branched into different forms. The diagram shows, for example, how the ray-finned fishes (center) grew into the largest class with the greatest variety of species, of which a few representative ones are shown at the far right. The coelacanths, which have changed little in 280 million years, are still caught today.

JAWLESS FISHES
Agnatha

SHELL-SKINNED FISHES

Hemicyclaspis
Endeiolepis
Drepanaspis
Pteraspis

ARMORED FISHES
Placodermi

Pterichthyodes
Dinichthys
Gemuendina
Rhamphodopsis

SPINY FISHES
Acanthodii

HOLO

Climatius
Acanthodes

RAY-FINNED FISHES

Cheirolepis
Platysomus
Haplolep

To Amphibians

LOBE-FINNED FISHES

Osteolepis
Holoptychius

HIGHER BONY FISHES
Osteichthyes

Rhabdoderma
Coelacanthu

LUNGFISHES

Dipterus
Uronemus

SHARKS, SKATES AND RAYS

Cladoselache
Hybodus

CARTILAGINOUS FISHES
Chondrichthyes

RATFISHES AND BRADYODONTS

Chodrenchelys
Helodus

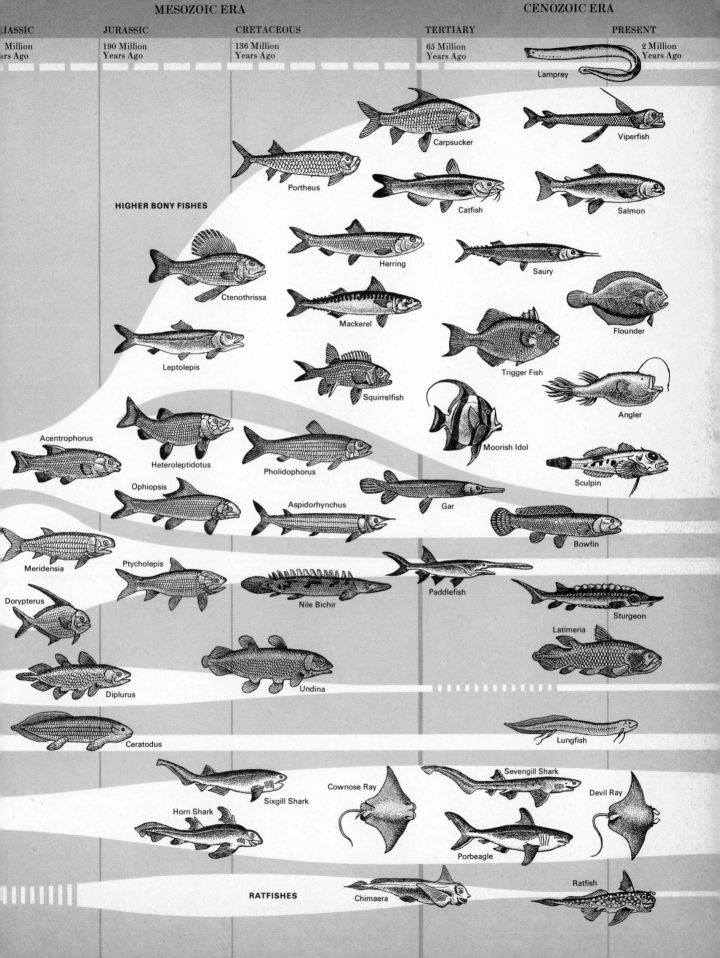

MESOZOIC ERA

CENOZOIC ERA

IASSIC

JURASSIC

CRETACEOUS

TERTIARY

PRESENT

Million
ars Ago

190 Million
Years Ago

136 Million
Years Ago

65 Million
Years Ago

2 Million
Years Ago

Lamprey

Carpsucker

Viperfish

Portheus

Catfish

Salmon

HIGHER BONY FISHES

Herring

Saury

Ctenothrissa

Mackerel

Flounder

Leptolepis

Squirrelfish

Trigger Fish

Acentrophorus

Angler

Heteroleptidotus

Pholidophorus

Moorish Idol

Ophiopsis

Aspidorhynchus

Gar

Sculpin

Meridensia

Ptycholepis

Bowfin

Dorypterus

Nile Bichir

Paddlefish

Sturgeon

Latimeria

Diplurus

Undina

Lungfish

Ceratodus

Sevengill Shark

Cownose Ray

Devil Ray

Sixgill Shark

Horn Shark

Porbeagle

Ratfish

RATFISHES

Chimaera

starve and die too, and so, too, do millions of birds that feed on the fishes. The piled-up, rotting corpses of fishes and birds cover the beaches and choke the coast for hundreds of miles, and the sea turns foul with the decaying plankton.

Similar disasters that occur from time to time off western Australia, in the Gulf of Mexico and in Africa, are due to the sudden bloom of masses of plankton—the so-called red tides. These catastrophes have received widespread publicity in Florida because of the trouble they sometimes cause in the tourist season, when the beaches may become littered for many miles with dead fish.

The red color of the water that gives these tides their name is caused by a population explosion among tiny members of the plankton called dinoflagellates. Red tides occur all over the world, and they generally follow a period of hot, windless days when the surface water becomes unusually warm. In this almost stagnant water dinoflagellates thrive enormously on certain salts, notably phosphates, that have accumulated at the surface. It has been stated often that what kills the fishes is suffocation through having their gills clogged by the sheer numbers of the plankton. The truth is that these dinoflagellates give off a poison that is deadly to many species. A red tide or something similar may have caused the widespread fish kill observed in 1957 by a Soviet research vessel cruising in the Arabian Sea. It reported a staggering sight—millions of dead fish over an area of 80,000 square miles between North Africa and India.

Man can do little about the natural disasters of the sea. No less important to our fresh-water fisheries, however, is the loss of fish population because of the heedless pollution of rivers and streams with industrial wastes and raw sewage. Any change in the water in which a fish swims is likely to have serious effects on the entire fish population of the area, and the disasters that follow are a reminder that the balance of life in the waters of the world is often a fragile one. While we can still rejoice in the natural wealth of fishes that number countless millions, it should never be forgotten that these riches can disappear quickly; these same fishes can die in the millions too.

A Prehistoric Holdover

The Australian lungfish has both gills and a single lung. Like others of its strange group, it dates back some 400 million years to a time when ponds and streams dried up, killing many fishes. Lungfishes survived because they had lungs to take oxygen directly from the air—a feat they can still perform.

2
A Watery
Way of Life

HOODED FISH are undisturbed by prodding fingers in this aquarium experiment. Without their "bathing caps" the fish would scurry away. But the caps cover the "lateral line" system of the head, a special "sixth sense" that picks up underwater vibrations to warn of unseen prey, enemies and barriers.

To man, looking down into the water from his familiar warm world of light and air, the realm in which fishes dwell often seems cold, dark, mysterious and populated by weird creatures. He himself can move about in it only with difficulty and in a very limited area. The fact that he must equip himself with cumbersome diving gear in order to see, breathe, keep warm and propel himself at a creeping pace, tends to hide some of the obvious advantages which fishes enjoy over creatures that live on land.

There are advantages to living in water, and they have played an important role in making fishes what they are. Water is not subject to sudden temperature changes and is therefore an excellent place to live for fishes, which are "cold-blooded" animals— that is, their body temperature is determined by their surroundings. The problem of supporting body weight, too, is far more simple than on land: since protoplasm body tissue has approximately the same density as water, a fish in water is almost weightless. This in turn means that a fish's skeleton can be light and simple. It also practically removes any limit to a fish's size, making it possible

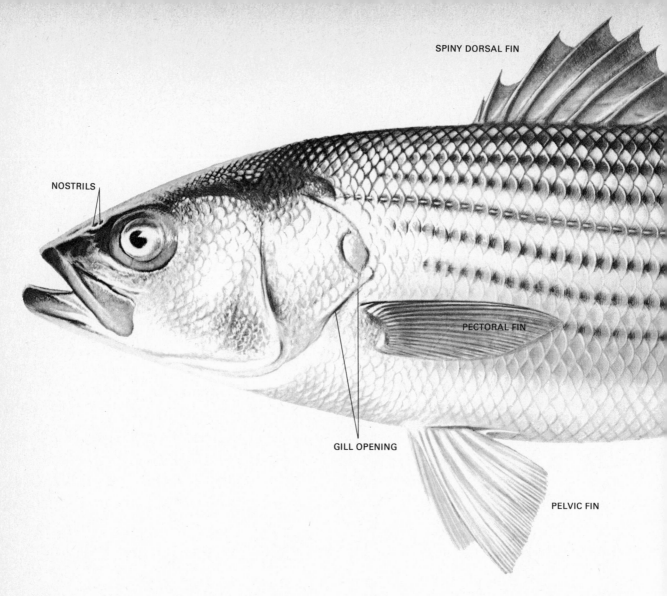

NOSTRILS

SPINY DORSAL FIN

PECTORAL FIN

GILL OPENING

PELVIC FIN

for an animal as huge as the whale shark to move about as easily and comfortably as a tiny guppy.

Yet there is one basic difficulty that fish must deal with—the fact that water cannot be compressed. This, more than anything else, has actually shaped fishes' development. Anyone who has ever waded in water that is more than ankle-deep has experienced the problem that fishes must overcome in moving: the water really must be pushed aside, and just as quickly as it is displaced, it closes in again from behind.

A flat and angular shape can be moved through such a medium only with difficulty. To push a board straight down in water flat side first is almost impossible; it always twists off violently to one side or another, for its narrow edges offer much less resistance and can slice through the water with greater ease. This is the reason why fishes have the basic shape we call streamlined: sharply pointed at the head for efficient parting of the waters, bulkiest ahead of the midsection, tapering back toward the tail so that the water can flow smoothly along the sides with

30

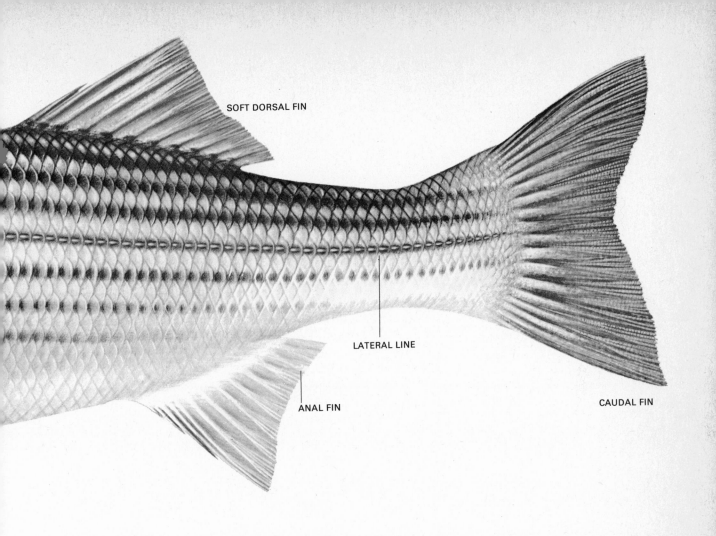

SOFT DORSAL FIN

LATERAL LINE

ANAL FIN

CAUDAL FIN

the least disturbance. There are many variations of this shape, of course, but in one form or another this is the basic appearance of all free-swimming fishes no matter in what direction they have evolved.

The fact that fish are cold-blooded has certain disadvantages, even though it does make them particularly well suited to life in the water. When the water temperature changes beyond the limits they can stand, fish have to move. This leads many of the Temperate Zone fishes to move from their regular living places as the weather changes

Streamlined for Swimming

The tapered shape of a striped bass, a typical bony fish that swims rapidly in open water, is ideal for getting around. The snout is pointed so that the bass can cut through the water. The water then flows smoothly past the body to the flaring tail, as the fish wriggles to propel itself (*page 45*). The dorsal and anal fins are stabilizers; they keep the fish from rolling over and over as it moves. The caudal, pectoral and pelvic fins are used for maneuvering and braking. The scales, which protect the body, are in turn protected and lubricated by a thin film of mucus.

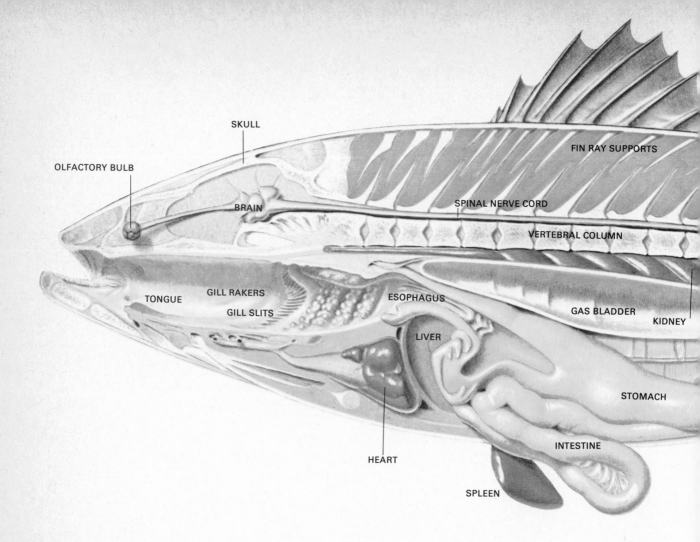

SKULL

FIN RAY SUPPORTS

OLFACTORY BULB

BRAIN

SPINAL NERVE CORD

VERTEBRAL COLUMN

GILL RAKERS

TONGUE

GILL SLITS

ESOPHAGUS

GAS BLADDER

KIDNEY

LIVER

STOMACH

HEART

INTESTINE

SPLEEN

with the seasons. Should the temperature shift abruptly, the fishes may become too sluggish to escape and, unless conditions become more normal, they will die. Some freshwater fishes, which in many cases cannot move when the seasons change, have avoided this danger by going into a form of winter or summer sleep—they stop feeding and remain inactive on the bottom in winter, or bury themselves in the mud in summer, until the temperature turns favorable again.

The blood circulation system of fishes is simple. Blood moves in a straightforward cycle from the heart through the gills, where the blood takes in oxygen, to the various

organs and parts of the body that use the oxygen, then back to the heart again. The heart itself is a pump with only two chambers (as contrasted with the three-chambered heart of the amphibians, and the mammals' four-chambered one).

A primary characteristic of fishes is the fins—the winglike structures, small or large, which enable fish to balance themselves in the water and aid them in moving and steering. Most fishes have two sets of paired fins—the pectorals, just behind the gills on the side of the head, and the pelvics, usually located farther back and somewhat lower on

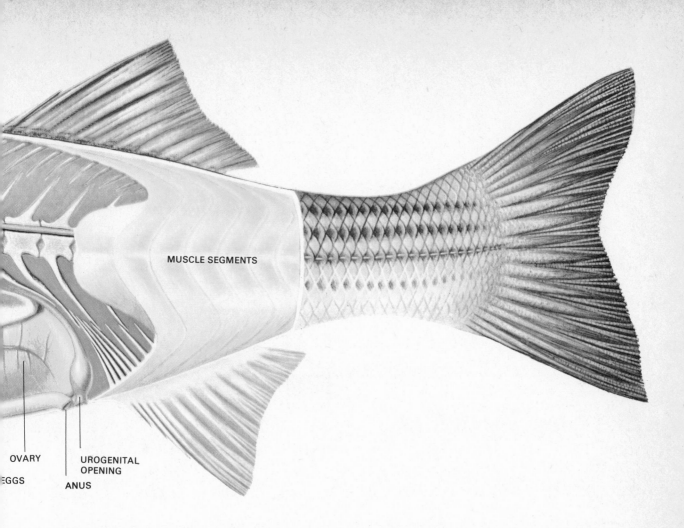

MUSCLE SEGMENTS

OVARY

EGGS

UROGENITAL
OPENING

ANUS

the body. Along the mid-line on top is the dorsal fin; along the underside toward the rear is the anal fin. At the very end of the body is the tail fin.

All of these fins have their own particular jobs to do in stabilizing and steering, and to accomplish these tasks, they are movable, worked by muscles within the fish's body. The dorsals and pectorals, working together, are the basic stabilizing agents. The dorsal fins, standing straight up, keep the fish vertical by preventing rolling; the pectorals, striking out sideways, are used for balancing and turning. The pelvic fins are also used as stabilizers. The tail fin may be used to steer or,

An Efficient Interior

The inside of the striped bass is just as well designed for life underwater as the outside is for underwater movement. The organs, compactly fitted into the muscular body, include specialized equipment not needed by animals on land. The gill rakers, for example, strain bits of food from the water as it passes from the mouth to the gill opening, and the gill slits draw oxygen from this water. The gas bladder in the center of the fish adjusts the fish's ability to float so that it can remain at any depth without sinking or rising. Below the gas bladder is the stomach; the intestine and spleen behind it are pulled out here so they can be seen. The olfactory bulb, connected to the brain, gives the fish its sense of smell.

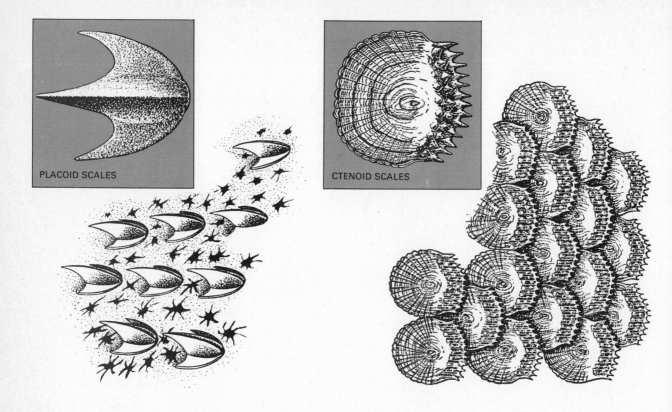

PLACOID SCALES

CTENOID SCALES

in the fastest fishes, as a stabilizer and a propeller, striking powerfully from side to side as the hind part of the fish's body wiggles in the swimming motion. In fast-moving fishes the dorsal and anal fins fold flat when swimming, or even sink into little grooves so that they lie flush with the body.

The shapes of fishes vary widely too. Perhaps the most unusual change in shape has been adopted by those fishes that have taken to lying on the bottom: they have become flattened. Some lie on their bellies, and these have become flattened from above; others lie on their sides and have become flattened sideways. In the latter, the flattening takes place as the young fish grows; one strange result is that both eyes move to the same, or upper, side of the head. Thus the flounder, for instance, which lies on its left side, has its eyes on the right side; its close cousin the fluke, on the other hand, has its eyes on the left side since it lies on its right side.

Even in the water, there are other ways of getting around than by swimming, and fishes have taken to them all. Some, like the sea-robin and the gurnard, crawl at the bottom; others can even crawl right out of the water onto the beach, as the mudskipper does. The Malayan climbing perch and the Chinese snakehead travel overland from pool to pool by wiggling along, using exactly the motions most fishes use for swimming.

Some fish can take to the air, if only for

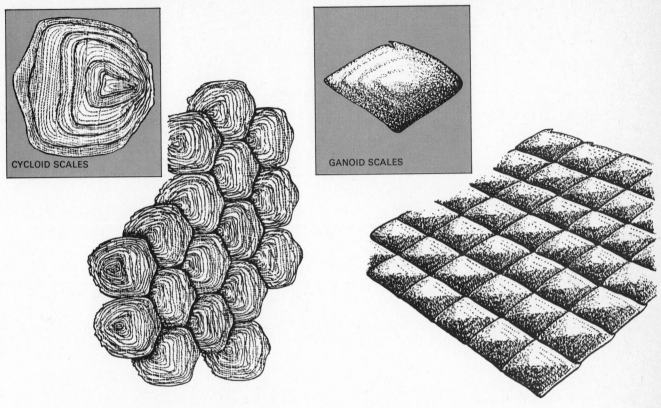

CYCLOID SCALES

GANOID SCALES

short distances. The garfish skips along the surface using its tail like the propeller of an outboard motor. But flying fish really fly— they can skim above the water for nearly a minute and if there is a good breeze to lift them up, they may sail along, reaching a height of 10 to 20 feet.

One striking characteristic of fish is quickly apparent: they are covered from head to tail in a usually flexible armor of rounded overlapping plates or scales of bone. These scales are embedded in the inner layer of the skin, and they form an important protective covering. In addition to this armor of scales, a fish is further protected by a layer of slime. Produced by many invisible glands scattered all over the body, this slime helps keep off

A Variety of Armor

The four kinds of scales shown here represent the body armor of all of today's fishes. The primitive placoid scales, found on sharks, rays and skates, are toothlike structures; each is about the size of a grain of coarse sandpaper, which the shark's skin resembles. The most common scales, ctenoid and cycloid, are found on bony fishes like herring, salmon and bass. Flexible and overlapping, they differ in only one respect: the ctenoid has a comblike edge, the cycloid a rounded border. A few primitive fish, like the garpike, have the diamond-shaped ganoid scales shown above.

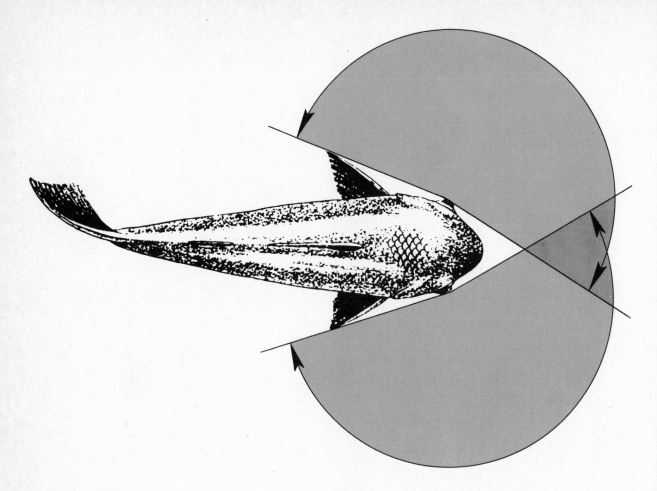

A Fish's Field of Vision

The eyes of most fishes are placed far apart. As a
result, each eye has a wide, separate field of vision
(*dark color*). There is, however, a small area in front
where these fields of vision overlap (*light color*).
Here the fish may be able to coordinate what both
eyes see, and focus on nearby objects straight ahead.

fungi and bacteria and also oils the body
surface. In size and thickness, scales may
vary greatly. The mahseer, a fish that lives
in Indian rivers and grows up to 12 feet long,
has scales as large as a man's hand. The common eel, by contrast, has scales that are so
small they can be seen only through a micro-
scope. A few species, like the lamprey, have
no scales at all.

A fish's mouth is its one and only tool for
feeding. As a result it has become highly specialized to enable each type of fish to gather
the food it lives on. The parrotfish has developed a regular beak to snip off plants and

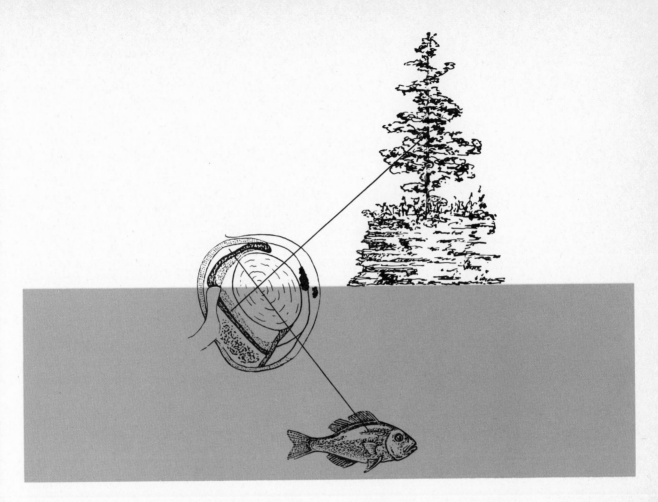

coral animals; the little sand launce has a digging tool, a hard, sharp projection on its lower jaw, with which to root around in the sand for its food of small shell animals, young fish and worms. Fishes that feed at the surface generally have upturned mouths. Similarly, bottom dwellers like the angler and stargazer, which feed on prey that swims above them, have mouths that are turned upward. On the other hand, those that feed off the bottom, like the skates and rays, the haddock and the common sucker, have their mouths on the underside of their heads to take in their food more easily.

A "Four-eyed" Fish

The Anableps, a small river fish of Central and South America, can see below and above the surface of the water at the same time. The picture here shows its eye, halfway out of the water, watching both the bank and an enemy fish below. Because of this uncanny ability, the two-eyed Anableps is called a "four-eyed" fish.

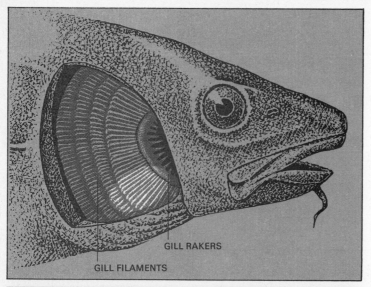

GILL RAKERS

GILL FILAMENTS

How a Fish's Gills Work

To breathe and feed, a fish takes in water through its mouth and lets it out through its gills by moving its gill covers open and shut. Food particles are strained out of the water by the gill rakers (which can be seen at left in the head of a cod with the gill covering removed). Water also flows through the gill filaments, which are arranged behind the gill rakers in overlapping, fan-shaped rows (shown in closer detail in the center picture). The bottom picture shows a cutaway view of one filament. Inside it, blood (*colored arrows*) flows through tiny channels called capillaries. From these capillaries the blood releases waste carbon dioxide to the water flowing around the filaments, and takes fresh oxygen from the water in return. Arteries, linked to the capillaries, carry the blood and the new load of oxygen back to the body, keeping the fish alive.

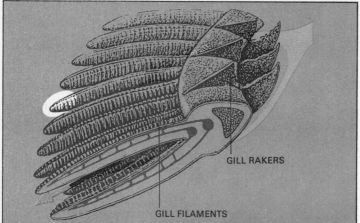

GILL RAKERS

GILL FILAMENTS

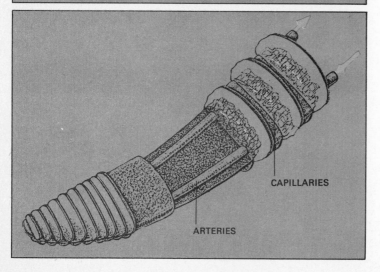

CAPILLARIES

ARTERIES

How does a fish breathe? We know that, like any animal, it needs oxygen to live—and in fact its breathing process is not so very different from that of air-breathing animals. Oxygen is dissolved in water, and fish get it by taking water through their mouths. They pass this water through gill chambers where the oxygen is extracted. The water is then expelled through vertical openings in the sides of the head.

The gills work very much like lungs. They are lined by blood vessels close to the surface, covered by thin skin. The skin has folds and plates that increase the area that takes in the oxygen. The entire gill mechanism is contained in a chamber protected by a bony shield called the gill cover.

The gill mechanism is used under many conditions. A few fishes can even use open air as well as water to obtain the oxygen they need. For example, when the pond in which the common carp lives runs short of oxygen or dries up in the hot summer months, the fish pokes its head out, takes in a bubble of air and holds it in its mouth near its moist gills. The climbing perch, the snakehead and the Indian catfish have special chambers that hold air which is passed over the gills. Lungfishes can breathe open air with perfectly good lungs, whose blood vessels are arranged on the same pattern as those of the amphibian frogs and newts. In some fishes that have changed little since very ancient times, the simple lung which later developed into the gas bladder (also called swim or air bladder) is still connected to the throat; in effect, such fishes, like the garpike and the bowfin, have extra lungs provided them for emergency use.

The gas bladder in modern fish, however, no longer has a breathing function but acts like a very advanced balloon. Built into the gut cavity underneath the spine, it is an air-tight sac lined with glands that can take gases directly from the fish's blood stream and put them in the bladder. The amount of gas is regulated to let the fish float at whatever level it may dwell, whether near the surface or deeper down to about 1,200 feet. Many fishes that live in the deeper regions of the sea, as well as most bottom-dwelling fishes, have no use at all for a gas bladder—because they need to stay down rather than float freely—and hence do not develop one.

Since water is so different from air as a living place, we may well wonder how the senses of a fish work to keep it informed of where it is and what is going on around it. What does a fish see? How does it hear? Does it have a nose to smell with? Does it have a sense of taste, a sense of touch?

The answer is that fishes have all of these five senses—and one more, a true sixth sense which makes them sharply aware of very subtle changes in the flow of water around them. Fishes are the only animals that have this sixth sense and it operates by means of nerve organs located in a canal system underneath the skin.

To begin with the sense of sight, however, it works in fishes much as it does in human beings, with two differences. The absence of brilliant light in the underwater world has led to an important change of eye structure in most fishes as compared with the eyes of land or air animals; they can get along with little or no contraction of the iris—the colored part of the eye that opens and closes to control the amount of light that enters the eye (they can do without eyelids, too, since the water in which they live constantly washes their eyes and keeps them free of foreign matter). They have an iris, a metallic-looking ring around the dark pupil, but since the quantity of light is fairly constant, it does not need to widen or shrink as much as ours. Because of this, in most fishes the iris never changes shape.

The fact that vision under water is limited to about 100 feet—and often a great deal less—also makes it unnecessary for fishes to adjust their eyes to different distances. Most of the time they need to see objects at only fairly close range, and this is about all their eyes can do. But, some experts think, the eyes are not good enough to give a fish a well-focused picture even at these short distances. Fish, under the best of circumstances, may never get a really clear look at things under water.

However, fishes do have an advantage that most land animals do not—they can see in more than one direction at a time. Their eyes are placed on the sides of their heads, rather than in the front. And there is good reason to believe that there is a narrow area straight ahead in which both eyes see the same thing, giving the fish a sense of distance and depth—just as we have.

To what degree fishes can see colors is not known. The general tone of the fish's submarine world is greenish-blue, since other colors are absorbed and disappear only a short distance from the surface. The ability to see different colors, therefore, is not of great importance to any except surface-swimming fishes. We do know, however, that all fishes except the shark can see some color. Microscopic examination of the nerve cells in their eyes has shown that they are supplied with the special nerve cells that are capable of telling one color from another.

To what extent fishes can use color in their daily existence is, however, still a mystery. Some like one color over another; trout for example seem to recognize the colors of different flies. Again, if a rainbow of light is flashed into a darkened aquarium the fish will go for the green and yellow bands and remain in them. On the other hand, if only a red light is used the fish behave as though they were in the dark.

Bright or strongly contrasting colors, of course, might be useful to fishes among themselves as a means of identifying fellow members of their species. It may also be that brilliant colors are a warning to other creatures that a fish is inedible or poisonous. There are some fishes that never seem to be eaten by other fishes, and in the shallow waters of tropical coral reefs where underwater visibility is relatively high, their colors, set-

No Two Noses Alike

African elephant-snout fishes, which come in a variety of weird shapes, feed on the bottoms of rivers and lakes. All have tiny mouths with few teeth, suited to sucking up small bits of food. But their snouts are further adapted for different uses. The top two fish shown here have long, beaklike "noses" for poking between stones and plant stems for food. The others have stubbier snouts for snuffling along the bottom.

ting them off so strongly from their fellows, may be their protection.

In most fishes the colors themselves are formed by a layer of cells in the skin underneath the transparent scales. These cells are color bearers, and contain grains of pigment which may be of various kinds.

The most important job that color performs for most fishes is to give them protection from their enemies. The color schemes of fish that live in the upper layers of the sea—dark on back, white or silver on the belly—make them difficult to see from any direction. Bottom fishes show really fancy camouflages—their colors may match the various shades of the bottom or, like the zig-zag paint on old-time warships, tend to break up the fish's outline.

Sometimes a fish's color matches its background to the point of imitating it in pattern as well as color. The Amazon leaf fish exactly resembles a leaf floating in the water. In tropical waters around Florida, for instance, a number of fishes, when quite young, take on the shape and color of the pods of mangrove seeds that lie on the white sand where they live. But as they get older, they "outgrow" the mangrove pods and the disguise is useless, so they move into deeper water and develop a banded pattern. The common flounder is one of the best camouflage artists of all, and can match pebbles, sand or dark mud with ease.

A Wonderful Walking Fish

The mudskipper, a popeyed resident of the tropical Asian mudflats, is at home either in water or on land. In water it swims quickly and sometimes even skips along the surface. On land it is equally agile, darting about on its pectoral fins, which it uses like legs. It seems to prefer life on land, where oxygen is more plentiful than in the muddy water, and where there is less competition for food. To breathe ashore, the mudskipper carries water in its gill chambers and mixes it with air taken in quick gulps.

Most fishes keep the same general color scheme throughout life, but some change color from youth to maturity. Young salmon and trout show dark stripes, which they lose when full-grown. The male salmon, trout, stickleback and many others also change color at the breeding season. Some coral fishes have displayed as many as seven shifts of the same color pattern within just one 24 hour period.

Even the sexes may dress up in different colors. The male dragonet and the cuckoo wrasse are as colorful as birds of bright plumage, while the females of both species are dull. Other fish, again, darken at night or, like the barracuda, take on a different pattern entirely. Many fish change color when frightened, when they are facing an enemy or when they are hooked.

On death the colors of fish generally change at once and are often quite different from those they had in life. Perhaps the most unusual death changes are those shown by the lively green and gold dolphin, or dorado. As it dies the green and gold turn to blue and chalk-white and then slowly, after the last quiver of life has ceased, to a dull, opaque olive drab.

A great deal of study has been devoted to the question of whether fishes can hear, in our sense of the word. Some think that they cannot, for their hearing organ acts only as an aid to balance. However, since a number of fish do make noises under water—noises that seem to be breeding signals, follow-the-leader calls or greeting signals—it does seem logical to say that fishes may hear sound in some way. The likeliest explanation is that they sense sound waves. Fishes have no eardrum or inner ear bone structure. But the gas bladder and a series of small bones connecting the gas bladder to the inner ear area in certain fishes may receive sound in the form of vibrations. Certainly some fishes are extremely sensitive to vibrations that involve direct movement of the water; they can detect the beat of a ship's propeller at a great distance. A footstep on the river bank, shaking the earth ever so slightly and thus setting the water in motion as well, is enough to make the trout move in its pool.

The sense of touch is conveyed to fishes by small, sensitive nerve organs scattered over the skin. These are particularly abundant around the head and lips, and many fish even carry the sense organs on feelers. The cod and the surmullet have fairly short feelers under their chins with which they probe over the ground; catfish have very long ones, like whiskers.

The sense of smell in almost all fishes is developed to a very high degree. Fishes have openings like human nostrils—a pair of small pits leading to the outside, located on the snout. The inside of these pits is lined with folded walls which contain the nerve cells that communicate smell.

The sense of smell in most fishes is so sharp that they seem to use it more than sight in seeking out their food. Sharks can smell blood a long way off and will show up, seemingly out of nowhere, to attack a bleeding fish or animal. Using fish blood or chopped-

up fish is an effective way of attracting, or "chumming," bluefish or other game fishes. Lampreys will react if just a cupful of water in which other fish have been swimming is poured into their tank; they instantly become alert and try to trace the origin of this sudden delicious aroma.

As for the sense of taste, it is probably not an important one in any fish's life. To begin with, no fish except lungfishes have taste organs in their mouths. Fishes do have taste buds, but these may be located on the head, body, tail, modified fins or chin feelers, so that if they do taste food, they do so before taking it into their mouths. Most fish simply gulp their food directly into the stomach, where it is digested.

The most fantastic sense fish have is that special sixth sense which makes them aware of the slightest movements and currents in

How a Fish Swims

Water offers more resistance to a moving body than air. Thus, when a fish swims, it must actually shove the water aside. The fish does this by wiggling back and forth in a snakelike motion, as shown by the colored outlines in the drawing below of a dogfish making one complete body stroke. The water is pushed aside by the head, the curve of the body and the flexible tail. The water flows back along the fish's narrowing sides and closes in at the tail, "squeezing" the body and thus helping push the fish forward.

the water. These sensations arise in the system of tiny canals in the skin which can be quite clearly seen on the sides of the fish; it is a line of scales shaped differently from the others and is called the "lateral line." At intervals in the main canal may be found special sense organs. Other similar canals, also equipped with these sense organs, branch over the head and face.

Scientists have not yet discovered all the secrets of the lateral line, but it is clear that its main function is connected with sensing the flow of water. If the branch nerve that leads from the lateral line to the brain is cut, the fish cannot react well to movements in the water or changes in the direction of flow. From experiments like this scientists have found answers to several puzzling problems. For example, it is the special sense that enables a coral fish to dart like lightning into a small hole it cannot possibly see clearly. The special sense also tells a fish in muddy water to turn away from obstacles still invisible in the murk. It may also be the lateral line that enables vast schools of fish, made up of thousands upon thousands of individuals, to hold such perfect formations as they swim along.

Anyone who has ever fished or watched a fisherman has wondered whether fish feel pain. This is a very difficult question to answer; pain is a psychological as well as a physical reaction, and there is no way of learning from the fish just what it feels. Humans who have experienced pain try in the future to avoid the thing that caused the hurt; this is called the psychological measure of pain. We may be fairly certain, however, that fishes do not experience the psychological measure of pain; there is little evidence that they learn by experience or association as human beings do.

Do they, then, feel pain physically? In humans, pain is experienced by the brain as the result of information sent to it by the nerves. But the brains of fish, unlike humans, do not have a section that can receive such messages from the nerves. This is why a fish can swim off apparently unconcerned with a hook in its mouth or a harpoon in its back, and a wounded shark will continue to attack even while its companions are tearing at its bowels.

A Stately Parade of Fish

When spadefish of the tropics move through the water, they swim in closely ordered formation, almost like columns of soldiers marching in a parade. Spadefish are only one of about 4,000 species of fish that move in such well-knit groups, or "schools," probably for the protection that their numbers provide.

FOUR MANTA RAYS, looking like a team of trained acrobats, leap high out of the Pacific Ocean off the Mexican coast near Acapulco. These immense rays grow up to 20 feet across and sometimes weigh over a ton and a half. They can jump 15 feet out of the water, and often do so to dislodge bothersome parasites.

3

Sharks and Rays: Loners of the Sea

The sharks and rays have always played a special role in man's long association with the sea. They are among the most primitive of any large living animals—for 350 million years they have followed a lonely course down the road of evolution, and despite the multiple problems presented by changing conditions they themselves have scarcely changed at all.

In addition, there is the awful reputation that some sharks have as killers. Because of this they inspire horror in man, a memory, perhaps, of distant ages when the sea held creatures even more terrible than they. In any case, to become aware of a shark approaching from dim waters just beyond the range of vision, or of a manta ray flapping across the ocean floor like some prehistoric

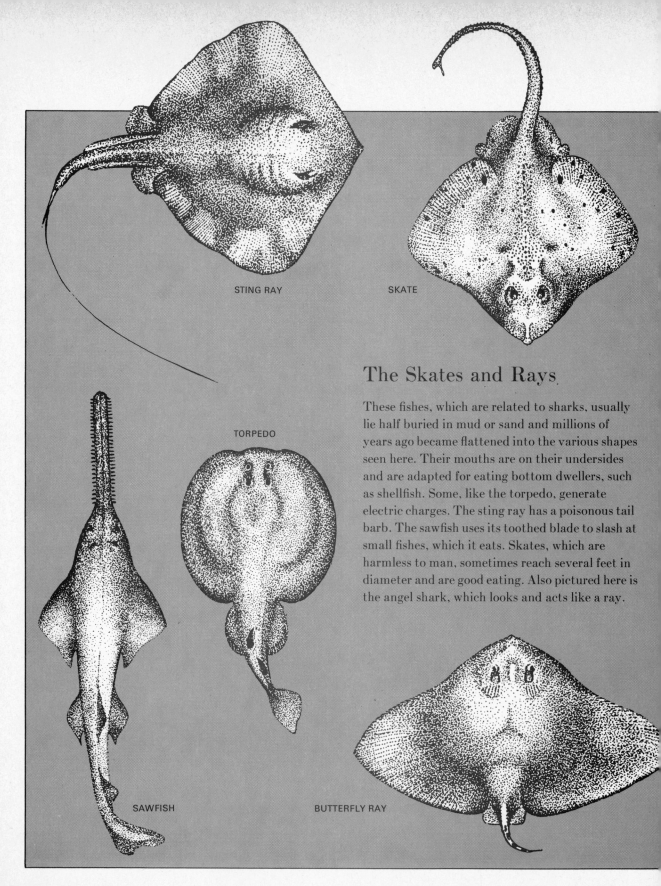

STING RAY

SKATE

The Skates and Rays

These fishes, which are related to sharks, usually lie half buried in mud or sand and millions of years ago became flattened into the various shapes seen here. Their mouths are on their undersides and are adapted for eating bottom dwellers, such as shellfish. Some, like the torpedo, generate electric charges. The sting ray has a poisonous tail barb. The sawfish uses its toothed blade to slash at small fishes, which it eats. Skates, which are harmless to man, sometimes reach several feet in diameter and are good eating. Also pictured here is the angel shark, which looks and acts like a ray.

TORPEDO

SAWFISH

BUTTERFLY RAY

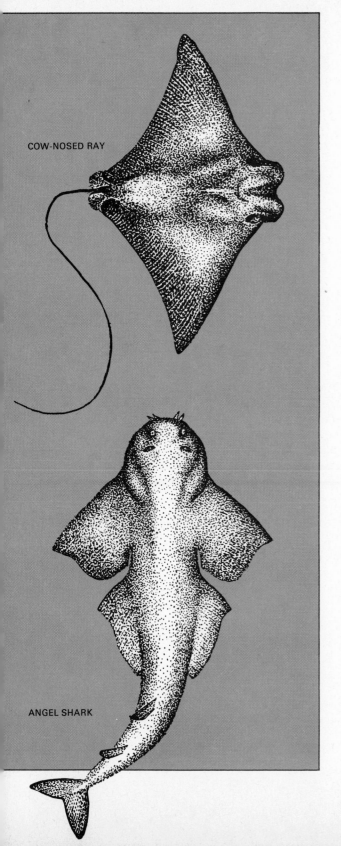

COW-NOSED RAY

ANGEL SHARK

monster, is to have a nightmare view down a dreadful hallway into the past.

A close-up look at any shark or ray does little to quiet these fears. Although the typical shark is one of the most beautifully streamlined of all fishes, long and graceful as it swims through the water, torpedolike in its bursts of speed, from head to tail it seems a creature of pure evil. Its mouth is grim and curved backward in a savage snarl beneath its shovel-edged nose. Inside that mouth are row upon row of teeth for seizing, shearing, piercing or crunching the shark's prey. These teeth renew themselves, moving forward to replace those that are worn out, torn out or fall out with age.

Sharks have another terrible weapon. Shark skin is covered with thousands of similar "teeth"—tiny, razor-sharp and close-set —that can tear the skin of a swimmer with a single sideways swipe or lunge of the long body. Sharks' eyes, set far apart on either side of the head, are fixed in a cold stare. The paired forefins thrust out from behind the head. They are used mainly for steering, for sharks cannot stop short or back up. For this reason sharks must attack their prey in wild, swerving lunges. The tail is a powerful propeller, and in the thresher shark it has developed into a formidable tool; longer than the body of the shark itself and curved like a scythe, it is used as a whip to herd together and stun large schools of fish to satisfy the thresher's huge appetite.

An outstanding feature of the sharks is

their excellent sense of smell. From the forward part of the shark's brain—a large share of which is given over to the job of smelling —two forks extend toward the nostrils on either side of the snout. The nostrils work so well that the shark can actually steer itself along a scent trail, much as an airplane follows a radio beam. Thus, when it first picks up a smell, it may swim back and forth, finding out the direction from which the scent comes: if the scent grows weaker on the left, it turns right, until at last it is on course. Then it follows the scent toward its source, often a quarter of a mile or more away. Experiments have shown that if one nostril is purposely plugged up, the shark will swim in circles, following the scent that it receives from one side only.

Like most fishes, sharks and rays probably hear little. Their ears are mainly balance organs, which tell the fish of changes in direction, when to speed up or slow down and whether it is right side up in the water.

Clustered on the heads and faces of both sharks and rays, and tapering back in a line toward the tail, is their version of the "lateral line" common to fishes. This consists of small sense organs sunk at the bottom of pits, each with a small pore to the outside of

the skin, which tell of vibrations and changes in the flow of water.

All sharks are meat-eaters, but the largest of them, the basking shark and the whale shark, live on the smallest form of animal food in the sea, animal plankton. Most of the big sharks are fish-eaters, but their diet also includes sea birds, turtles, small porpoises and sometimes even land animals, including man. Rays—except for the biggest ones, the mantas, which are also plankton-eaters—feed on fishes, shellfish, sea urchins and other creatures that live on the bottom. Unlike some sharks, rays are not aggressive in their feeding. Even the biggest of the rays will

Weapons for Offense and Defense

The sawfish (*below, left*) is a ray that swims like a shark, with mighty strokes of its powerful tail. Its long, flattened snout is edged with up to 30 pairs of saw teeth. The sting ray seen below illustrates how rays camouflage themselves by burrowing in the sand on the floor of the sea, which is much the same color as the ray's body. The ray's tail, barbed and poisonous, is kept uncovered for defense.

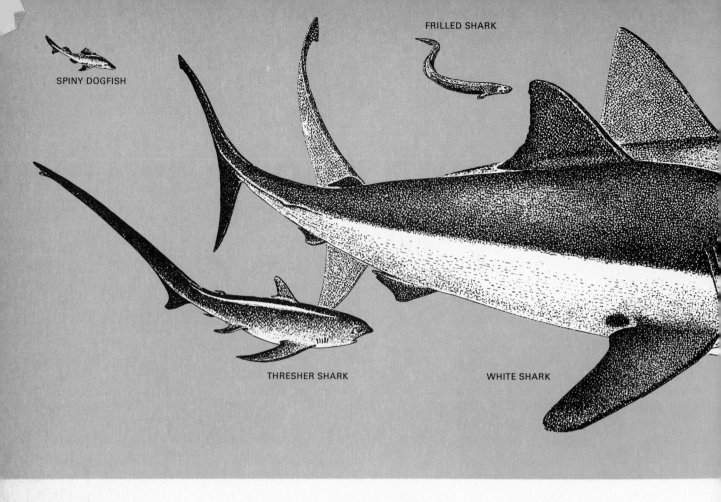

SPINY DOGFISH

FRILLED SHARK

THRESHER SHARK

WHITE SHARK

never make an unprovoked attack on man.

The stories of what sharks will eat are endless and mostly wrong. Certainly they have huge appetites and seem to wolf their food with little care for what it is. In the stomach of one tiger shark were found fish bones, grass, feathers, bones of marine birds, bits of turtle shell, some old cans, a dog's backbone and the skull of a cow without the horns. A large shark caught off the island of Mauritius had a kerosene can in its stomach. Another had a horse's head and bits of a bicycle. This seems to uphold the belief that sharks will eat anything, but the term "scavenger" can really be applied only to the tiger shark, which *will* gulp anything. Actually, sharks will attack and eat wounded or dying sea animals, but there is little proof that they prefer to feed on dead creatures.

Sharks have always been thought fierce and aggressive animals, but whether this is truly so is not sure. Their behavior varies greatly. They may come up in dozens from the dark depths to inspect a piece of bait, then spend a long time circling it before one of them makes a lunge. If, while this investigation is going on, the bait is given a sudden jerk, they may scatter as if in fright, and it will be a minute or two before they begin their cautious circling once again.

Blood in the water, however, drives them mad. A kind of wild fury, called the "feeding frenzy," takes hold of the sharks and

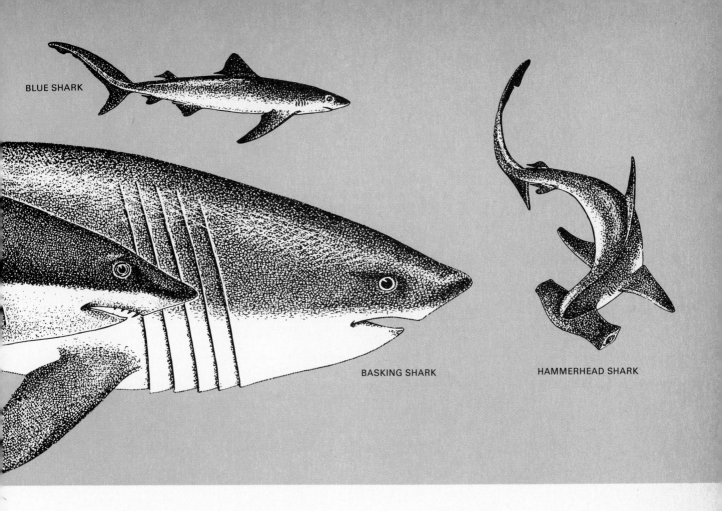

BLUE SHARK

BASKING SHARK

HAMMERHEAD SHARK

they charge in against all opposition. If one of them is wounded they even turn on it, attacking at once and with great fury.

Several kinds of sharks attack man, although why and under what conditions is far from certain. Skin divers have had face-to-face meetings with sharks and escaped unhurt; they have also been attacked for no reason. Wherever there are many sharks, horrible deaths occur from time to time. In shark-infested areas, like some Australian beaches, shark fences and patrols are needed to protect bathers. The Shark Research Panel of the American Institute of Biological Sciences has collected records of shark attacks in all parts of the world, starting with a 1580 report of a Portuguese seaman's death and

The Many Shapes of Sharks

The wide range of shark types and sizes is shown in seven species drawn to scale above. One of the largest of all sharks is the basking shark, which may be more than 40 feet long but is harmless because it eats only plankton. The white shark grows to 20 feet and is one of the swiftest, most dangerous sharks; as a man-eater, it overshadows even the hammerhead, which reaches 15 feet and weighs half a ton. The 18-foot thresher, a tropical species, is believed to use its long tail to stun smaller fishes and sweep them toward its mouth. The 12-foot blue shark is probably the most numerous of all sharks. The five-foot frilled shark is eellike and no threat to man. To Americans, the most familiar shark is the harmless spiny dogfish, which roams warm waters around the world.

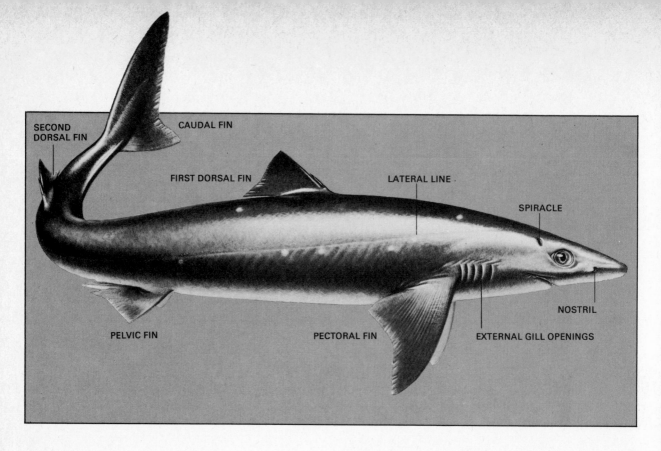

SECOND DORSAL FIN

CAUDAL FIN

FIRST DORSAL FIN

LATERAL LINE

SPIRACLE

NOSTRIL

PELVIC FIN

PECTORAL FIN

EXTERNAL GILL OPENINGS

The Design of a Shark

The sharks and rays, of which the spiny dogfish above is typical, differ from the common bony fishes in several ways. Their skeletons are simple cartilage instead of bone. A small gill opening called the spiracle, seen just behind the eye, is found in some sharks (and most skates and rays). In these fishes water is drawn in through the spiracle instead of the mouth and expelled through the gill slits. Sharks lack bony gill covers; their gills show as rows of slits on either side of their bodies just behind their heads.

going up to 1963. These added up to 866, with 359 deaths. Of these attacks, 293 occurred off Australia, 166 off North American coasts, and 193 in Pacific waters. For each year since 1963, the panel has received reports of between 30 and 35 attacks.

What exactly drives a shark to attack a human being? Human flesh is not its normal food, for all sharks are by nature fish-eaters, so that a shark would probably have to be very hungry before attacking something so far off its normal diet. The smell of blood is certainly a factor in shark attacks, but fear may be another drive. The noise of bathers splashing was at one time supposed to frighten sharks away, and sailors during World War II were always told to kick and splash if they found themselves in the water or on a raft with sharks around. More recently, however, the belief has grown that sudden

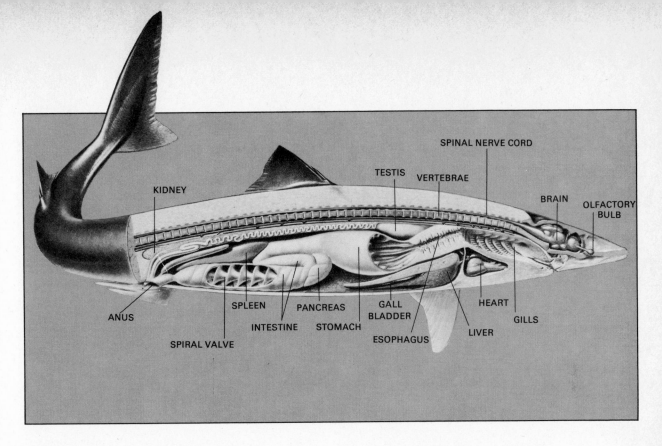

KIDNEY
TESTIS
VERTEBRAE
SPINAL NERVE CORD
BRAIN
OLFACTORY BULB
ANUS
SPLEEN
PANCREAS
GALL BLADDER
HEART
INTESTINE
STOMACH
ESOPHAGUS
LIVER
GILLS
SPIRAL VALVE

movement attracts sharks rather than scaring them off; it is possible that these movements may suggest that the man is in trouble and trigger an attack. Out in the open ocean, however, sharks probably attack out of hunger, snapping at anything that seems edible.

The truth is that no one has yet been able to learn why sharks attack human beings or what action should be taken to discourage them. Much advice on the subject is, therefore, highly unreliable. The best suggestion is simply to get out of the water as quietly and quickly as possible—if it is possible to do so. Shouting at sharks, hitting them on the snout, splashing or kicking—all recommended at one time or another—may work in one instance and may not in another; the shark is as likely to be maddened as it is to be scared. On the other hand, if the shark

Looking inside a Shark

The interiors of sharks and rays also differ somewhat from those of the bony fishes. The shark, again represented by a spiny dogfish above, has not developed a gas bladder to help it float and must keep constantly in motion to avoid sinking. Its brain is small, but its huge smelling organ, the olfactory bulb, gives it one of the keenest noses of all fishes. The shark intestine, sometimes called the "spiral valve," is short, but twisted in spirals, which gives it a large surface for absorbing water and digested food.

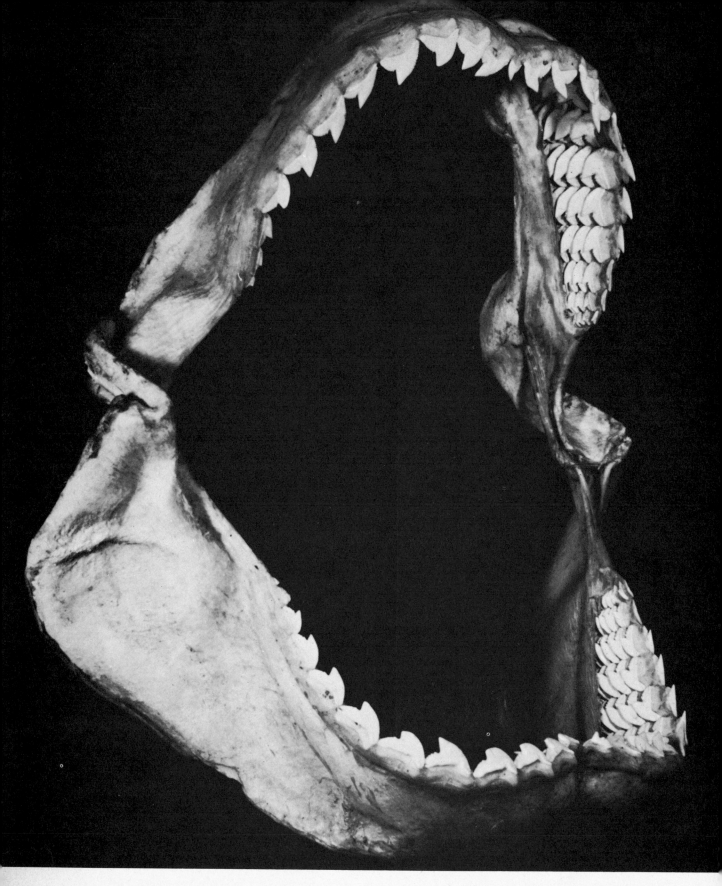

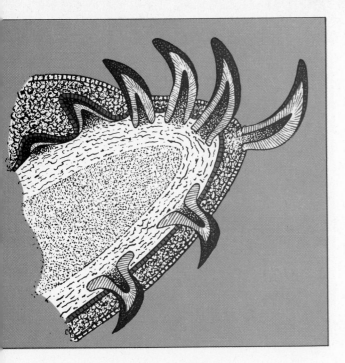

Sharp Scales for Teeth

The hooklike scales that cover a shark's body also appear inside its jaw in the larger form of teeth. In the drawing above, a cross-section view of the tip of a shark's lower jaw, the two pointed objects at the bottom are body scales, greatly enlarged to show the roots holding them permanently in place. The ones above represent six rows of teeth, which are not firmly anchored in the jaw, but grow in the skin, steadily moving forward as they increase in size. As a tooth in the front row is ground down, it falls out and is replaced by one from the second row, which in turn is ground down and replaced. During a period of 10 years a tiger shark, like the one whose jaw is shown at left, may produce and shed no less than 24,000 teeth.

makes no obvious move to attack, a quiet withdrawal or, if there is no place to withdraw to, simply staying quiet in the water may result in the shark's going away.

Terrible wounds are inflicted by shark bites, but almost as terrible may be the abrasions caused by the rough skin, which is as sharp a surface as a rock covered with barnacles. Sharks are known to have bitten off people's arms and legs, though this is not the usual form an attack takes because a shark's mouth is built more for tearing than for chopping and cutting. There are stories, too, of sharks throwing their screaming victims up in the air and playing with them, as a cat plays with a mouse. Such tactics are certainly not deliberate, but since a shark charges from underneath, its prey may be thrown out of the water by the upward rush.

Some 12 kinds of shark are known to eat humans. The most formidable of all is the great white shark, or "man-eater." The biggest one of record was 21 feet long; the average size of the grown male is around 14 feet, with 16 feet not unusual.

The hammerhead shark is also feared. It is mainly a shallow-water shark, whose eyes and nostrils are set at the ends of wings on either side of the head, giving the creature an unusually frightening appearance. The exact purpose of this odd shape is not known. It may give a wider area of vision and scent, or it may enable the hammerhead to move with greater agility.

Strangely enough, the largest sharks of all

are harmless ones. The basking shark and the tropical whale shark stick to their plankton and small fishes, and are downright mild of temper. The basking shark of northern temperate waters may reach a length of 45 feet; the whale shark of the tropical seas can reach 50 or 60 feet.

The whale shark travels in small groups or alone. But often it seeks out the company of boats more or less its own size and hence is often easily approachable. The *Kon-Tiki* explorers, drifting silently on their raft, saw whale sharks at close quarters. Quite often fishermen stopping for line fishing near the Seychelles Islands, which lie in the Indian Ocean about 1,000 miles off East Africa, see the huge, speckled monsters surfacing near them. One time a fishing boat had to use oars to pole itself off from a whale shark.

From the true sharks, this family branches out to more and more flattened forms. These include the angel shark (a shark that looks like a ray) and the guitarfish and sawfish (rays that look like sharks). The huge sawfish, which lives in shallow waters, has a long nose armed with rows of teeth on either side, which the sawfish uses to cut up its prey.

Finally, there are the rays—skates, electric rays, eagle rays, mantas and the like—flattened animals that live on the bottom. Their pectoral fins have become enlarged and attached to their heads, forming winglike shapes which give these animals the appearance of sea-going bats. Many rays, unlike

(*Text continued on page 64*)

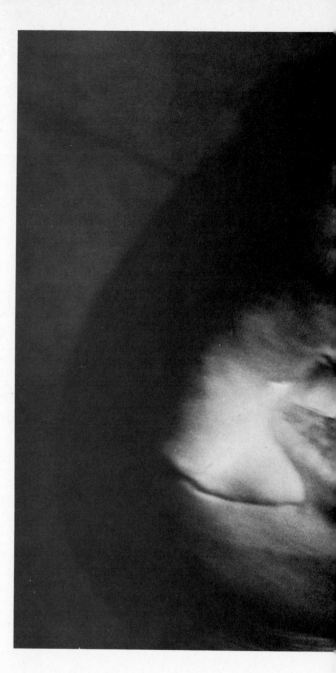

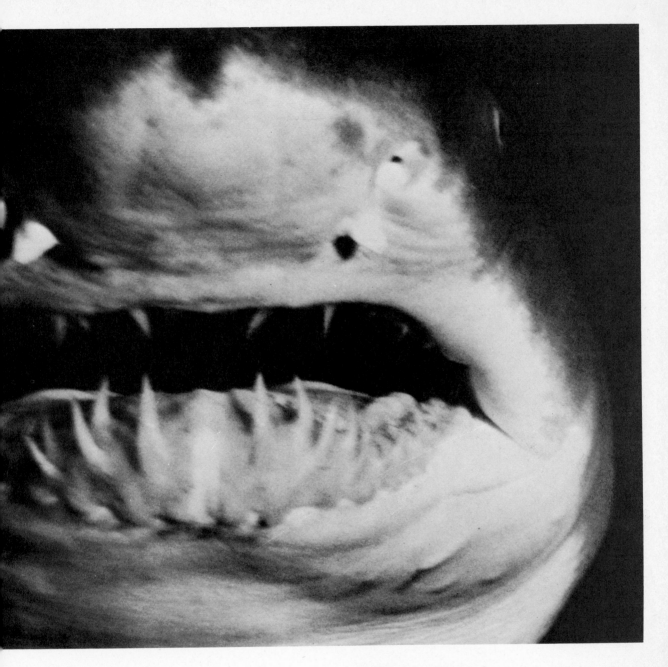

A Fierce Prowler

Its mouth ringed with rapierlike teeth, this four-foot North Atlantic sand shark prowls the warm, shallow waters close to shore in search of food. Frightening as it looks, it does not normally attack humans; but if provoked it can turn viciously on its tormentor.

A blue shark rips flesh from a dead porpoise. Next, the shark may eat along the length of the body like a man chomping corn on the cob.

sharks, have smooth skins. The great manta ray, or devilfish, has projections on either side of its mouth which add to its fearful appearance. Some of the rays may be huge; one of the Atlantic species is so large it is named the barndoor skate. Sting rays may be as large as six feet across, and the great black-and-white devilfish may be 22 feet from wing tip to wing tip. However, the smallest rays, found in the South Seas, are only five inches or less across.

The sting rays, a family of about 100 species, are named for the daggerlike points they carry near the base of their tails. Each point has a narrow groove down the side, along which runs a strip of poisonous tissue. The pain of the stings is terrible, and death may result from shock or heart failure. Thus even the smallest sting ray should be handled carefully. Even gloves do not mean safety—the sting may go through them.

Some of the skates and a few rays have small electric organs that can give a shock. In the skates, these are placed along the sides of the tail and are supplied with nerves leading from the spinal cord. In the rays, the electric organs are located in the wings, or shoulders, with the nerves coming from the brain. In both types, the organs are made from special muscle fibers. The electrical current is started by a chemical reaction beginning in the nerves. Once a shock has been released, a certain period of time is needed to allow the electric energy to build up to full charge again.

The torpedo, or electric, rays have the largest and most powerful of these electric organs. Found in shallow tropical and temperate waters, some torpedo rays are very small, while others reach up to five feet from wing tip to wing tip. A large torpedo ray may generate twice the voltage of ordinary household current—more than enough to knock a man down.

Somehow it seems fitting that a member of the ancient class of sharks and rays should be equipped with one of the strangest weapons in the sea. It brings home once more the fact that these creatures, from the fiercest shark to the smallest ray, are different from any of the other fishes that have evolved and fought for their survival in their own way.

A Shark's Deadly Approach

A blue shark wheels around to attack its prey. Like other large sharks, the blue first slowly swims around its victim, then speeds up, tightening its circle. As it plunges forward for its first bite, nothing short of death can stop it. If one attacking shark is wounded, others will turn on it and devour it.

4

Life and Death
in a Silent World

VICTIMS of a mass poisoning, these fish are among the millions killed from time to time in Florida waters. The deaths occur when tiny planktonic organisms of a certain species suddenly increase by the millions, each giving off a poison. Because the plankton is rust colored, this phenomenon is called a "red tide."

In the vast, dim underwater world where the fishes live, the struggle for food is every bit as strong as it is among the animals that live on land. Every shallow pond or lakeside, every tidal pool is filled with a mass of little creatures eating the tiny plants and plankton found at the bottom. These are the food-rich areas, with plenty of oxygen given off by plants, plenty of light and plenty of living space, with sand, mud, weeds and rocks all providing food and hiding places.

In these shallow areas, the water is a window through which humans can watch the underwater community of the fishes and plants, crowded closely, often piled on top of one another in the war of survival—enemies and friends, hunters and hunted. How is this community made up? How do its members, different as they are, get along?

Like other animals, fishes enter into associations with each other and with other underwater creatures. These relationships may be casual, or they may be very close. Some fishes even form an association with lifeless things. In the warmer waters of the North Atlantic, there lives a species of large fish that has entered into a "relationship" with

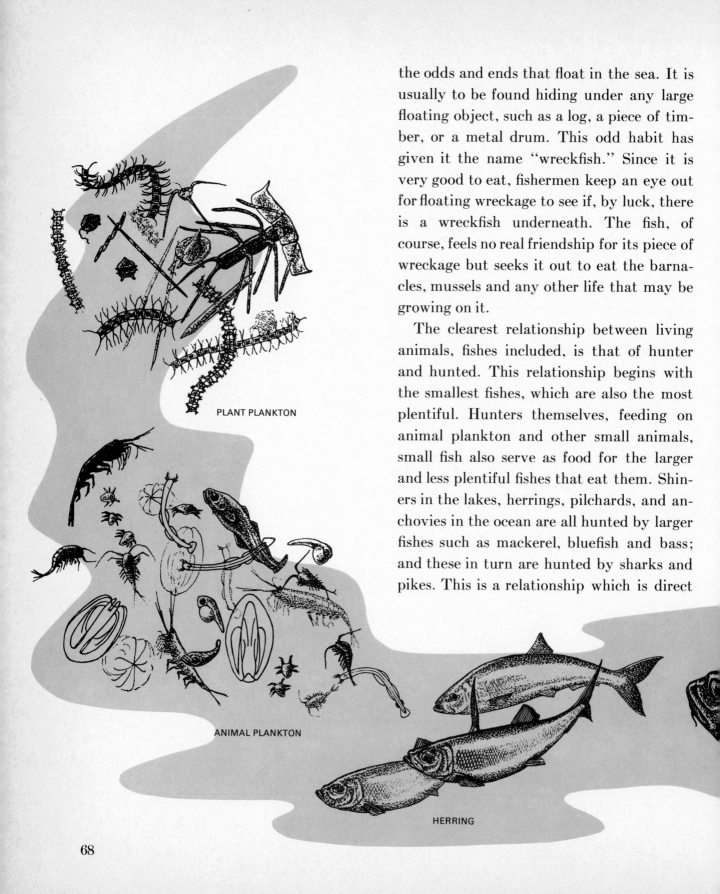

the odds and ends that float in the sea. It is usually to be found hiding under any large floating object, such as a log, a piece of timber, or a metal drum. This odd habit has given it the name "wreckfish." Since it is very good to eat, fishermen keep an eye out for floating wreckage to see if, by luck, there is a wreckfish underneath. The fish, of course, feels no real friendship for its piece of wreckage but seeks it out to eat the barnacles, mussels and any other life that may be growing on it.

The clearest relationship between living animals, fishes included, is that of hunter and hunted. This relationship begins with the smallest fishes, which are also the most plentiful. Hunters themselves, feeding on animal plankton and other small animals, small fish also serve as food for the larger and less plentiful fishes that eat them. Shiners in the lakes, herrings, pilchards, and anchovies in the ocean are all hunted by larger fishes such as mackerel, bluefish and bass; and these in turn are hunted by sharks and pikes. This is a relationship which is direct

PLANT PLANKTON

ANIMAL PLANKTON

HERRING

68

and final. It is the very basis of life and death in the watery depths.

There are, of course, many other less harsh relationships between different kinds of fishes, and between fishes and other animals in the water. There is the very loose association in which one partner merely lives with the other and gains from it, without giving anything in return.

A good example of this is the pilotfish, which almost always travels with tropical sharks. The pilotfish is about a foot long, blue in color with darker stripes along its sides. It swims alongside its shark just below and behind the head. Pilotfish were known to the ancient Greeks and Romans and for a long time were thought to be leading the sharks to their food—which is how they got their name. Actually, they are followers, feeding on scraps from the sharks' meals. They do not attach themselves to a single shark: if one shark among a group of several takes a bite at something, the pilotfish will swim away from the sharks that are not feeding and join the one that is. As for the

Who Eats Whom in the Sea

Fish survive in the sea by eating plants, small animals and each other. Microscopic plant plankton (*far left*) indirectly provide food for the entire sea community. These one-celled plants are eaten by tiny animal plankton, mostly shellfish. These in turn are consumed by herring and other small fishes. Larger fishes, like cod, eat the herring and are finally eaten themselves by still larger fishes, like the mackerel shark shown below. These sharks roam the seas without fear; they have no natural enemies other than man.

COD

MACKEREL SHARK

shark, it gets no reward from the association, but merely tolerates the company of the smaller fish.

The relationship of the shark sucker, or remora, to its shark companion is not very different from that of the pilotfish except that the remora attaches itself to the shark's body and is carried around by it. There are some 10 different kinds of remoras in tropical waters, ranging in size from a few inches to about three feet. They all have a flat, oval disk on the top of the head which acts like a suction cup, enabling the remora to stick to the flat surface of the shark's body. When the shark stops to feed, the remora drops off and searches for food on its own. It returns to the same shark, or another, when it wants to move on after feeding. If a shark is caught and hauled out of the water, its remoras drop off and find another shark. Or they may

attach themselves to the hull of the fisherman's boat. Sometimes, remoras cling to fishes other than sharks; they have been found on certain sporting fishes like the giant sunfishes and marlins.

Some young fishes associate with jellyfish. These include the European whiting, young haddock and crevallés, which often shelter under the bell-shaped bodies of the jellyfish that live among coral reefs. A relative of the crevallé lives in close association with the Portuguese man-of-war. The man-of-war is a frightening sight, and its sting can render a man unconscious. It drifts on the surface of the water with its tentacles spread out, forming an almost invisible network of poisonous lashes that sometimes extends for 100 feet. But the little fish darts in and out of this dangerous network without ever being

Breaking a Spiny Defense

A sea urchin, which has long needles for armor, would seem safe in its watery home, but a queen trigger-fish *(opposite page)* is equipped to pierce this defense. With its 14 cutting teeth the fish nips off the spines *(left)*, while its tough skin protects it against the sharp quills (which, in some varieties, are poisonous too). After the fish has eaten all that it wants of the fleshy interior of the urchin, smaller fish gather around *(above)* to eat any shreds that might be left behind.

harmed. Nevertheless, this association is not without dangers. Should the fish accidentally brush too roughly against the tentacles while swimming among them, it may be stung and eaten by the man-of-war.

Another interesting case is the relationship between the brightly banded damselfish of the tropics and the huge stinging sea anemones with which they live. The anemone is a pale, seemingly slow creature, up to three feet across, with a tangle of tentacles covered with stinging cells. Nearly every anemone has three, four or more damselfish carrying on their lives among these poisonous arms, darting out on trips for food but returning always to the protection of the anemone. Each fish knows its own anemone and always returns to the same one. Sometimes a male and a female will even keep house together, raising their young, which are carefully watched over by the father, until they are old enough to go out and find an anemone of their own. More surprising, each anemone seems always to know its own damselfish and does not harm them, although it will sting to death any other fish that wanders into its tentacles, including any strange damselfish. No one knows how the anemone is able to recognize its own fish—nor, for that matter, exactly how they come to live together in the first place. It used to be thought that the anemone got nothing out of the relationship, but it may be that the damselfish bring back food for the anemone, and also act as bait

A Blood-sucking Predator

The sea lamprey is a blood-eating parasite that puts a death clamp on a fish and sucks blood until the fish dies (above). It does this through a mouth shaped like a suction cup (right) and teeth with which it cuts through the scales of its victim. In some places lampreys have nearly destroyed the lake trout population. Lampreys from the ocean invaded the Great Lakes in the 1930s, preying on the lake trout population and almost wiping it out.

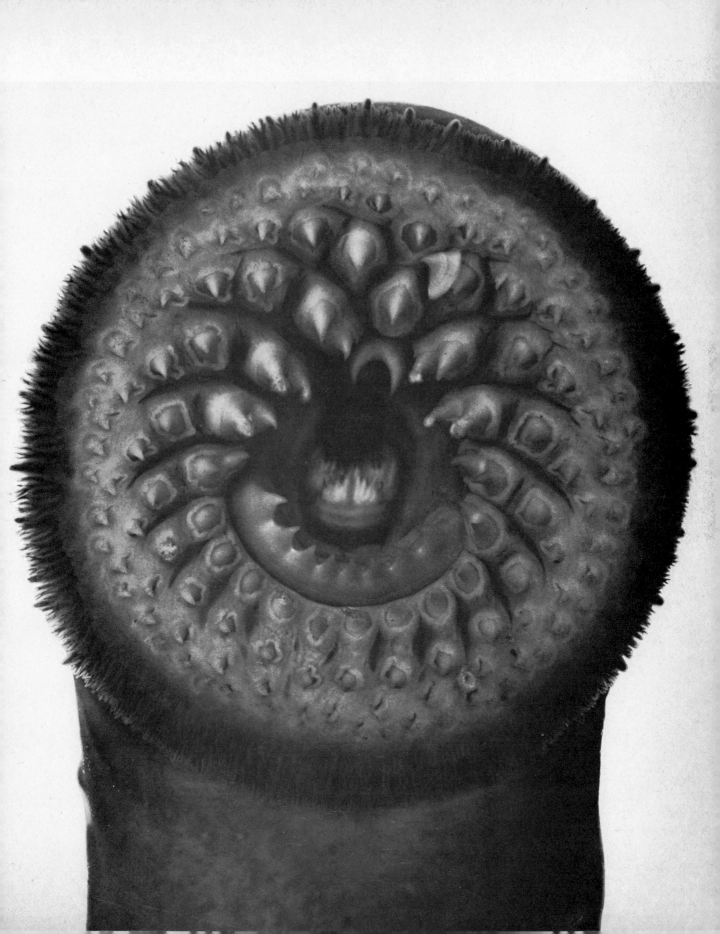

for other fishes, which they lead to their death in the tentacles.

In still another strange association, some fishes take care of others by cleaning them. Fish easily pick up infections and harmful parasites and fungi, especially if there is any break of the skin. Small wounds easily become infected. When this happens a fish will seek out the services of the cleaning fishes, which eat the parasites and dead tissue from the wounds.

The number of fish that actually clean others is very large. At least 26 known types of fish make cleaning their primary job (there are also some six types of cleaning shrimp, one bird, a crab and a worm). Wrasses are among the most active cleaners, but the pilotfish, in addition to accompany-

ing sharks, also cleans manta rays, and a tropical angelfish is so well known for its neat work that it is called "the barber" along the Mexican coast. The butterfly-fish and the neon goby are also famous cleaners. Extremely courageous is a certain small wrasse that goes into a customer's mouth, works over the teeth and goes right on down into the gullet until its customer shows by snapping its jaws a few times that it is completely satisfied.

The bright colors of the tropical cleaning fishes serve to advertise their profession, but they have other ways of getting work. When they see a prospect approaching, they may swim out to meet it and put on a display. They dart about, pushing the prospective

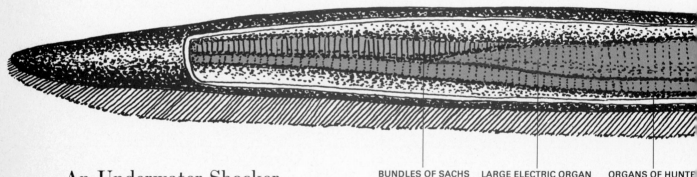

BUNDLES OF SACHS   LARGE ELECTRIC ORGAN   ORGANS OF HUNTE

An Underwater Shocker

The electric eel uses its natural body electricity as a powerful weapon. Most of the eel's body is devoted to its "batteries," the parts labeled above. One of these, the so-called "bundles of Sachs," generates a weak electric field. A fish that swims too near disturbs this field (*opposite page, left*). The eel responds by triggering its main powerhouse (*opposite page, right*). The blast of direct current can exceed 350 volts, stunning or killing a victim.

customer's body, waving their fins and tails, nibbling, going back and forth until the fish is persuaded. At this point, the customer appears to go to sleep, floating motionless, usually at an odd angle, on its side, standing on its head, or upside down. The cleaner then goes to work, making its way up and down the customer's body, nibbling tiny sea creatures or cleaning the infections. If it wants to get in underneath a fin that is being held too close to the client's side, the cleaner will gently nudge until the fin is lifted. It will also work its way under the gill covers and probe between lips and teeth to tell its customer to open its mouth so that it can get inside.

The job a cleaner does is a very thorough one, and sometimes a client fish will seem to help it along by changing color to show up sore spots. An Indian Ocean fish turns from near black to light blue, another simply turns pale. A species of discus fish that seems to be prone to fungus infections turns almost totally black so that the white fungi show up clearly.

Even more intimate than the service cleaning fish give is the association in which one animal or plant actually lives in or on another. In this relationship one of the pair —the parasite—gets all the reward while the other—the host—is hurt by it. The relationship may be carried to such lengths that the parasite's body actually joins its tissues with those of its host. The host, for its part, may become so weakened by its unwelcome guest that it wastes away and dies.

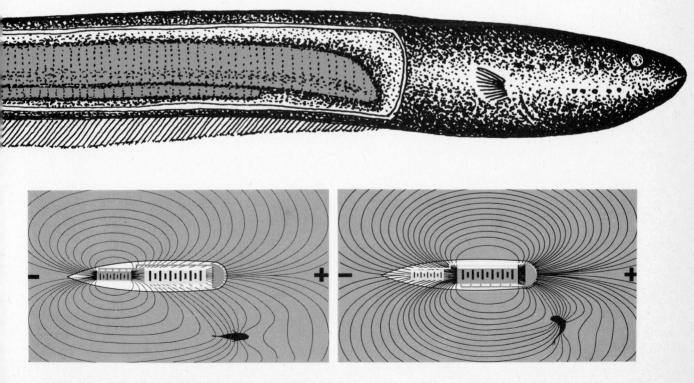

Most of these kinds of unwanted guests feed off the host but do not kill it. Lampreys eat away the flesh and suck the blood of fishes to which they attach themselves. The candiru, a tiny catfish two or three inches long that lives in South American rivers, enters the gills of a larger kind of catfish. The candiru uses its sharp teeth and spines on its gill covers to cut its host and eat its flesh.

While most fishes do not live off other fishes, they are hosts to a large number of animals that live off them. Fish carry tiny animals in their intestines, heart, liver, muscles and blood. Among these are many kinds of flatworms, tapeworms, roundworms and threadworms. One of the most unusual is a small, wormlike creature that grows in the eggs of Volga River sturgeon while they are still in the female's ovary. The creatures come out when the eggs hatch to lead a free-swimming life of their own.

All the relationships mentioned so far grow from a need for food and individual safety. But there are, in the fish's world, other associations that have to do with the safety of masses of fish. There are four kinds of social behavior among fishes. First there is the lone fish. Then there are crowds of fish formed by chance, like the cod on their feeding grounds. Next come schools, in which the fish are all lined up with one another and

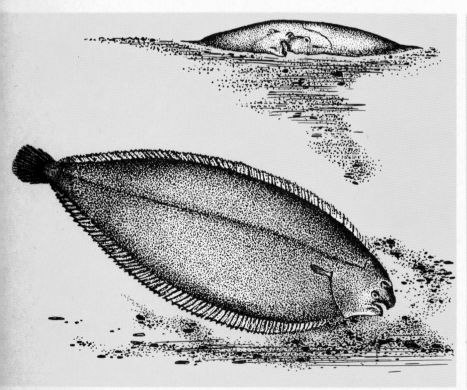

SOLE

BUTTERFLYFISH

keep a set swimming distance between them. Still farther up the scale are pods, in which the fish form a dense, close mass, crowding so closely together that their bodies are actually touching.

The best known of these associations is schooling, in which masses of fish swim around together. Schooling is most often seen among the fishes of the open ocean, especially the herring and its relatives. The strength of the school may depend upon the fish being able to see one another, since many schools tend to break up during the night and re-form at daybreak. However, the lateral-line system, rather than sight, may play an important role in schooling,

Shaped for Safety

The way a fish is built often helps it stay alive. The sole, flat as a plate, buries itself in the sandy sea floor by day to avoid its enemies. At night it prowls along the bottom after food. The butterflyfish has an "eye" spot on its tail to fool its enemies, and spines on its back that make it an unpleasant mouthful. The globefish, when threatened, swells up its prickly body with water, making it almost impossible to swallow. The seahorse is ringed with bony plates that help camouflage it by breaking up its shape.

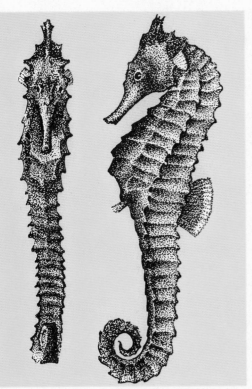

SEAHORSE

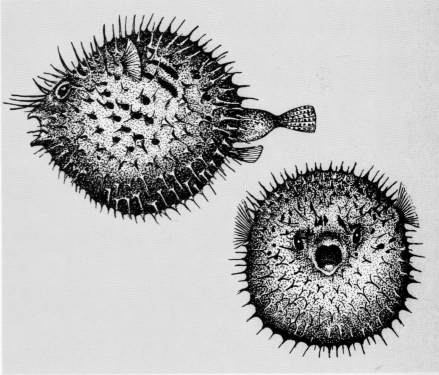

GLOBEFISH

77

especially in those cases where schools appear to stay together after nightfall.

A large school of fish acts as though it were a single animal. Its form is regular, with about the same number of fish swimming ahead, beside and on top of each other. On nearing the surface or in shallow water, the school usually spreads out in a thinner layer. In a school of anchovies swimming between the surface and the bottom, the larger fish are generally underneath and the smaller ones on top. There are limits in the size of the members of a big school, too—in a school of herring no fish is more than half again as large or small as the average size for the school. Any fish above or below the size limit swim off and form schools among themselves. Sometimes schools break up, or small schools join into larger units.

The safety of the group seems to be the

The Art of Camouflage

Many fish both hunt and hide by looking exactly like their surroundings. The sargassum fish closely resembles the seaweed it lives in; only by looking very closely can you see the three in the picture at left. The scorpion fish (*right*) looks like a barnacled rock. It lies still on the bottom but moves swiftly when something appetizing comes by. A fresh-water shield darter (*below*) conceals itself by lying still on gravel stream beds.

main reason for the schooling habit, but the way each species reacts to danger is different. Herring bunch together as danger nears, and anchovies under attack crowd so closely that they form dense, thick balls. On the other hand, the mackerel of the tropics scatter in all directions and dive when a net is close by.

Another strange aspect of school behavior is the forming of a "mill," or wheel, in which thousands of fish play "follow-the-leader" round and round in a circle. This is perhaps the result of being crowded in a small space—a little pool or shallow water. Outside Zanzibar harbor on the east coast of Africa there is an old sunken ship whose steel shell encloses a deep, narrow pool of clear water. Here thousands of mullets circle constantly in dense masses. When a net is dropped into the pool, the wheel of mul-

A Seaweed Mimic

The filefish, seen in front and side views at right, is doubly adapted for protection. It can change color to match its surroundings, and it imitates vegetation near it by turning upside down and gently waving its fins, looking for all the world like a blade of seaweed. For further protection, its flesh contains poisonous chemicals that its enemies find distasteful.

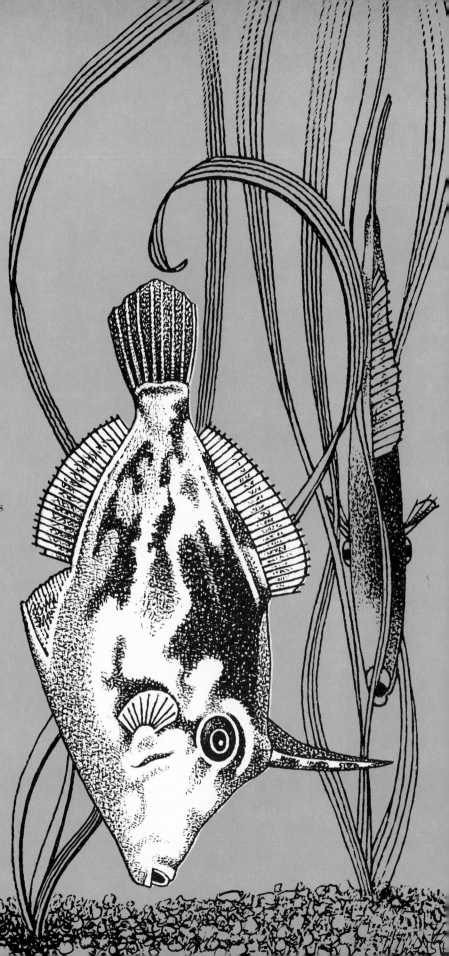

lets breaks up. But the wheel re-forms almost immediately, and the fish begin their endless circling again when the net is drawn up to the surface.

How much of a part sound plays in the formation of schools and the way they act is still being learned from experiments. A great many fishes make noises that may be signals for gathering, and many more make noises humans cannot hear. But these sounds can be picked up by instruments and made louder so that they can be heard by human ears. They are said to sound "like water pouring," and may be caused by movements of the fishes' muscles or bone structure. The noises seem to occur when a school is moving toward a goal or changing direction, and not when it is idling along or at rest.

Scientists at the Bermuda Biological Station found that they could make schools of anchovies and jackfish change direction by recording these swimming sounds and playing them back under water. When a sudden loud noise was made under water near the school, the fish nearest to the noise turned away. This reaction to the noise went right through the school, but seemed to pass from fish to fish with each fish reacting to the movement of its neighbor. Sounds made above the water had no effect, nor did sudden actions such as waving arms. But if a boat above was rocked, the school changed direction right away, reacting to the waves set up by the rocking action.

Similar experiments to learn the part played by sight showed that blinded fish could not school with a slowly moving school, but instantly joined up with the group if the school sped up. The explanation may be that the lateral-line sense organs came into use above a certain speed. Fish blinded in one eye only were unable to form up on their blind side but could school normally on the side of their good eye.

Schools form suddenly and they do not follow any leader in their steady movement through the water. Fish traveling in the front often drop back and are replaced by others from the ranks, and when the school changes course, the fish on the side find themselves on the leading edge, while those on the leading edge become the side. Such a shift, even when performed by a large school of a million fish or more, is carried out with such speed that an observer looking down on it from above thinks he is watching a single creature flowing through the water. It is almost as though there were some central control system moving the entire school.

How do the fishes do it? Somewhere in their life history, there must be some factor that explains the mystery of this special social behavior—but where and what is it?

Evelyn Shaw, a biologist at New York's American Museum of Natural History, tried to answer these questions by studying fish from the time they were hatched. Watching two kinds of common silverside, a tiny schooling fish plentiful in the waters of New England, led her to believe that schooling

began when the young had reached a length of 10 to 11 millimeters (a little less than half an inch). But did schooling begin suddenly or did it come along slowly?

She took her experiments into the laboratory, with very interesting results. She found that schooling did come along slowly. In the earliest stages, when newly hatched fish met one another, they came close then darted away. When the young had reached a length of eight to nine millimeters, they might swim together for a second or two if they met head

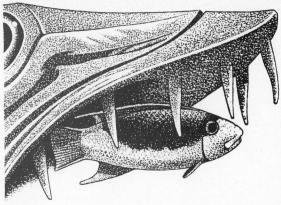

A Busy, Dangerous Job

Fish that clean others of parasites lead a busy and sometimes death-defying life. At left, two small, round butterflyfish tend to a gray-blue goatfish as countless other goatfish mill around, waiting their turns. The butterflyfish use their many small buckteeth not only to clean other fish, but also to scavenge rocks. In a more dangerous game, the wrasse swims into the open mouth of the ferocious barracuda (*above*). The little fish darts fearlessly among the dagger-sharp teeth, keeping its host free of infection by feeding on bacterial growths in its mouth.

to tail, with one following the other. If they met head on, however, they would turn away as though afraid. Soon, however, the head-to-tail meeting became common and the baby fish swam together for as long as five or 10 seconds.

The first signs of real schooling came when the young were 10 to $10^{1}/_{2}$ millimeters long. One young fish would come to the tail of another and both would shake their bodies. The two would then swim off, staying in formation for as long as a minute. Sometimes they might be joined by other young to form a ragged little school. At 11 to 12 millimeters, as many as 10 might thus form up, and by the time they were 14 millimeters long, they were schooling steadily and with better ability. Thus it was discovered that schooling is indeed something fishes pick up gradually, not something they just suddenly do.

It is a long jump from the tiny silversides swimming in a laboratory tank to the great schools of tuna sweeping through the wide Pacific. Yet, as other aspects of communal living in the sea have taught us, it is not an illogical one. For in the struggle that goes on all the time under the surface of the water, schooling may help fish to stay alive. Schooling means that the tiny young fish emerging from scattered eggs have a way of finding themselves in groups—groups that offer them protection, an easy way to find mates and sometimes even food. All in all, it is a more efficient way of surviving than alone. Some 4,000 species of fish long ago took on the schooling habit, and so far as man can tell, it serves them well.

A Surprise Attack from Above

To the normal dangers of underwater life are added the outside threats of birds, animals and man. Here a tufted puffin, patrolling its aquarium tank, moves into position over a pair of unsuspecting herring, exactly as it would on its native banks in the Bering Sea. Plunging downward with powerful strokes of its wings (*far right*), the puffin grabs a fish.

5

How Fishes Reproduce

THE MATING COLORS of a male cuckoo wrasse (*left, below*) contrast vividly with its normal hues (*left, above*). In the spring it takes on bolder colors to match its courting behavior. It builds a nest, then darts about the females until one is frightened—or fascinated—enough to fill the shelter with eggs.

To fishes, as to any other living thing, the reproduction of their own kind is second in importance only to eating and staying alive. Reproduction is a simple matter for most fish—when the time comes, male and female spawn, placing their eggs and sperm in the water where, as they mingle, fertilization occurs. But there are, of course, exceptions to the general rule, and so in the waters of the world some unusual ways of continuing the population are found.

Basically, the reproductive organs of fish are no different from those of any other animal. Males and females carry the sperm- and egg-producing organs in elongated, paired sacs, which run lengthwise in the body. In most instances, eggs and sperm are discharged directly from these sacs into the water through tubes. In some species, however, the eggs first drop into the body, and then pass out to the water from there through special pores. Compared to other animals, the size of the reproductive organs of most fishes is relatively enormous. The female salmon, for instance, may have ovaries that weigh as much as one quarter of her total body weight.

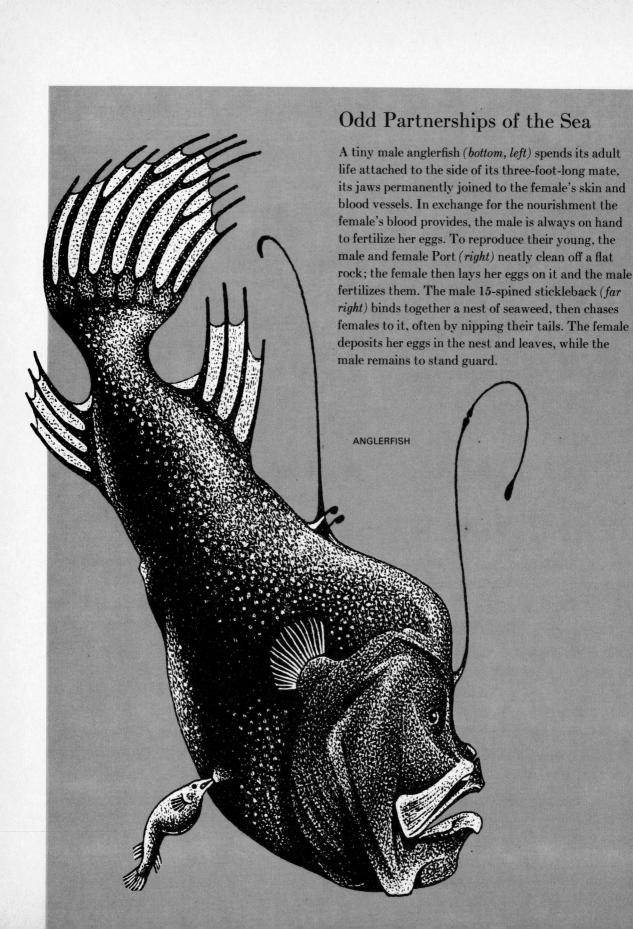

Odd Partnerships of the Sea

A tiny male anglerfish *(bottom, left)* spends its adult life attached to the side of its three-foot-long mate, its jaws permanently joined to the female's skin and blood vessels. In exchange for the nourishment the female's blood provides, the male is always on hand to fertilize her eggs. To reproduce their young, the male and female Port *(right)* neatly clean off a flat rock; the female then lays her eggs on it and the male fertilizes them. The male 15-spined stickleback *(far right)* binds together a nest of seaweed, then chases females to it, often by nipping their tails. The female deposits her eggs in the nest and leaves, while the male remains to stand guard.

ANGLERFISH

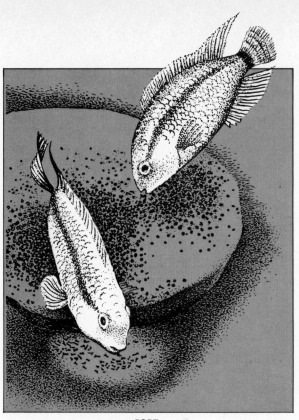

PORT

FIFTEEN-SPINED STICKLEBACK

The temperature of the water plays a key role in the reproductive process. Most species of fish have their own favorite temperature range for spawning, and if this changes they may not spawn at all. The eggs and young are also sensitive to heat and cold, and temperature changes can kill them.

Most fishes have a particular spawning season when the temperature is right for them. For the sea herring, which generally stays in northern waters, the spring and the fall are best, and it spawns at both these times. The menhaden, by contrast, chooses its season depending on where it is; off southern New England, menhaden usually spawn in June, but farther south off Chesapeake Bay the spawning time comes in the fall, and still farther south in early winter. In the warm tropics, many kinds of fish spawn throughout the year.

Most fishes not only have set spawning times but also special places to spawn. The cod, a deep-water fish, comes into shallower waters to spawn, and has certain banks where it does so. Off Cape May, New Jersey, cod spawn each winter. Around the Lofoten Islands off the coast of Norway there is a great cod spawning ground, and there are other well-known grounds along the Greenland coast, on the Grand Banks off Newfoundland, and around Iceland. And, of course, there are the well-known examples of fish such as the salmon, shad and alewife that return to the same spawning beds in the same rivers year after year.

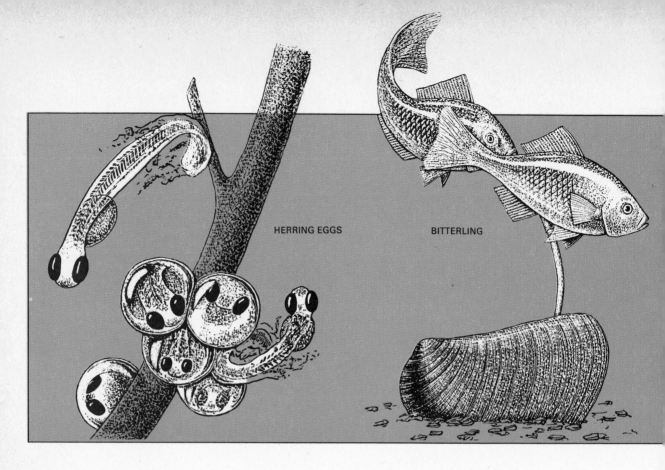

HERRING EGGS   BITTERLING

While it is relatively easy to bring eggs and sperm together, the survival of the fertilized egg, and the young fish after they hatch, is far more difficult. Youth is a time of special danger for all living things, and for fish particularly so. But nature has ways of making sure that at least enough young survive to continue the race. Special protection may be provided for the egg and young, or the eggs may be produced in such vast numbers that, come what may, at least some of them are sure to survive.

Fishes, in most cases, have adopted the second alternative and rely on sheer numbers. Eggs are shed into the water in staggering quantities and simply left to the mercy of the environment.

The eggs of most food fishes go through their development while afloat. Such floating eggs are generally small, translucent spheres about one millimeter in diameter (the size of a pin head), surrounded by a clear membrane, often with one or more drops of oil in each egg to keep it afloat. Some floating eggs attach themselves to floating objects or each other.

The eggs of most flyingfishes have long strings that become entangled with the sargassum weed; needlefish eggs have small projections so that they cling together in clumps. The eggs of the herring and of many fresh-water fishes, on the other hand, sink to the bottom. Herring eggs are coated with a sticky substance that adheres to seaweed, stones or anything with which they may come into contact, but salmon, trout and shad eggs, which are generally shed in swift

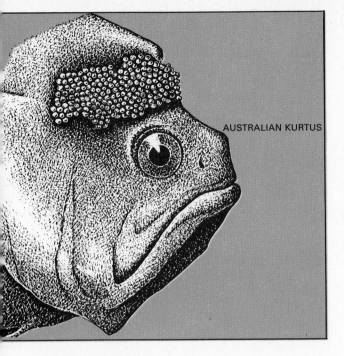

AUSTRALIAN KURTUS

Ways That Eggs Survive

Fishes' eggs, which are tiny and have no shells, are protected by nature in various ways. Herring eggs sink to the bottom, where they stick to stones, sand or stalks of seaweed (*far left*); here they hatch, safe from egg-eating fish that cruise the waters above. The female bitterling protects its eggs by depositing them through a long tube into the shell of a fresh-water mussel (*middle*). The male bitterling then sheds its sperm in the water nearby; as the shellfish feeds by drawing in water, the eggs are fertilized. The male Australian Kurtus (*left*) actually carries the female's fertilized eggs around on its forehead; they are held in place by a special "hook" that grows forward from its dorsal fin.

streams, must be deposited in gravel beds to protect them. One 54-pound ling cod, when caught, was found to be carrying 28,361,000 eggs; a 17-pound turbot had nine million. A female cod regularly lays between four and six million eggs at a single spawning—if all the eggs spawned each year survived it would take only a few years to jam all the world's oceans with codfish. As it is, less than one egg in every million needs to live in order to continue the race. All the rest may be destroyed by the many dangers of the sea. They are eaten by birds, fishes and many other enemies. They drift into water too deep, too warm or too cold for them to live, or they are washed ashore and dry up.

Like eggs of other animals, most fish eggs have a yolk on which the newly formed embryo can feed. Once the yolk is used up, the little fish develops a mouth and begins to feed itself, taking in tiny plankton.

In these earliest life stages the young fish is usually referred to as a larva, a term used to denote any young animal that has to undergo complete bodily change to reach its adult form. Sometimes the larvae of fishes may be so different from the adult, both in appearance and habits, that they are not recognizable as the young of the adults they will become. In the past many of these larvae were not at first spotted for what they were, but they were thought to be quite different animals and were given separate names. Such was the case, for example, with an eel larva that until fairly recently was known as *Leptocephalus* and accepted as a distinct species all its own.

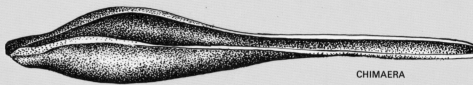

CAT SHARK

CHIMAERA

PORT JACKSON SHARK

Odd "Purses" for Eggs

The eggs of some fish, including certain
varieties of skates and sharks, are protected by
ingenious containers—"mermaids' purses"—
often found washed up on beaches. Each case
holds a single embryo while it develops, which
may take as long as 15 months. Most have
hooks or long, vinelike extensions that catch in
seaweed, anchoring the case in a relatively safe,
hidden place. The egg case of the chimaera, a
deep-water fish, has a long tail that helps hold
it to the sandy bottom.

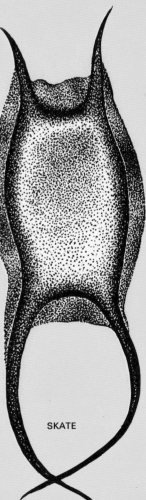

SKATE

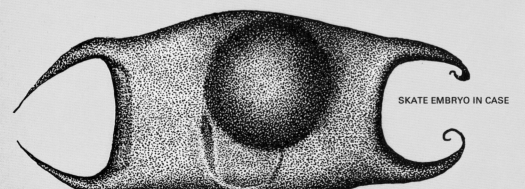

SKATE EMBRYO IN CASE

The larval cod is more typical. When young it looks like an adult. The baby cod is about a quarter of an inch long when the yolk sac disappears. At that point it is fully on its own, looking out for and feeding itself. The young of the haddock, on the other hand, also a member of the cod family, seek shelter among the stinging tentacles of the cyanea, a big jellyfish. Here they look for food in safety without getting stung.

The cod young may drift and grow for as long as two and a half months before they move, around midsummer, down to the bottom in shallow water near the shore. At this point they are young fish about three quarters of an inch long. As they grow, they move out to deeper water, and at the end of the first year in the North Atlantic they will be about six inches long. At three years of age they are about a foot long; at this stage, when they are known as codlings, they are beginning to be caught by fishing ships. The young cod finally grow up fully in their fourth or fifth year, when they reach a length of two or three feet. Then, they themselves are ready to spawn for the first time.

The system of shedding large quantities of eggs and casting them adrift is common among the fishes of the open seas, but there are a number of other fishes living in more protected waters that have developed different ways of producing young. Such fishes shed only a small number of eggs. Some may look for hiding places to lay them, others may keep the eggs inside the body until they are hatched, and some, after hatching, even guard their young until they can look out for themselves.

Most of these unfishlike spawning habits have been taken on by fish that live among rocks, in tidal basins, bays and inlets, or in fresh-water streams and lakes. The dangers here are different from those of the open sea, where the pounding surf of the shoreline, or tides and currents may wash the eggs away. There are, however, many ways to protect the eggs. The ocean pout, a fish often caught in the western North Atlantic, uses at least two of them.

The ocean pout lays only a few hundred relatively large eggs, which are held together in a jelly-like mass. These bunches of eggs have been found in cans, old rubber boots and similar debris brought up from the ocean floor, indicating that the female usually looks for a safe hole for her eggs.

There are other ways to protect the young. The American gaff-topsail catfish and the tropical spiny sea catfish lay some 50 eggs at a time. The male fish then takes them in his mouth where they develop, living on their own yolk, while their father goes without any food at all until they hatch.

The fertilization of the eggs, or breeding, often leads fish to act in unusual ways. Pipefishes and seahorses are good examples. Pipefishes are common in warm, temperate and tropical waters, especially on beds of eelgrass. They may reach a length of 18 inches, but in the tropics they are usually smaller.

When feeding, they wind their tails around weeds and poke for small shrimp and other plankton. They swim almost straight up and down, often bent into an S shape, advancing by wiggles of their fins. The male Florida pipefish has flaps along his underside which, at the breeding season, form a pouch. When mating takes place the male and female approach and pass one another a few times, then join S's, crossing in three places.

Pipefishes then reverse the roles usually taken by male and female animals. The female neatly deposits her eggs in the male's pouch, where they are fertilized. The male then does a sort of spinning dance in order to pack the eggs down in rows, after which they repeat the linked-S performance until the pouch is full. The female then swims away, her role finished, leaving the male in charge of the eggs. In about two weeks the father's pouch is full of perfectly formed young pipefish. The walls of the pouch then open up and the small, threadlike young come out and take to the water. When danger threatens, they may return to the safety of their father's pouch.

Some fishes quite deliberately lay their eggs out of the water. The characin (*Copeina arnoldi*), at home in the Amazon River and its tributaries, has gone to unusual extremes to assure the survival of its eggs. After courtship, the male escorts the female to a spot where a leaf or branch overhangs the surface of the water by an inch or two. The pair lock fins and leap out of the water, clinging to the leaf for an instant to deposit a small mass of eggs. This act is performed repeatedly until a sizable number of eggs is attached to the leaf. To prevent the eggs from drying out, the male fish splashes them with his tail during their three-day hatching period.

The grunion, surf smelt, capelin and even occasionally the sand launce have abandoned the water as a safe place for their eggs; instead they deposit them on the shore. Of all these, the grunion is the best known for its interesting spawning habits. It spawns on certain California beaches during the periods of higher tides that occur at the time of the new and full moons, laying its eggs in the sand at the upper reaches of the tide. At exactly the correct moment between waves, the female buries herself tail-first in the sand and deposits the eggs. The nearest male sheds his sperm about her and the eggs are fertilized. Two weeks later, during the next series of high tides, the eggs are washed out of the sand and hatch.

Grunions are known to spawn more than once every two weeks on each cycle of high water. The timing of this activity is amazing to observe. They carefully wait until the tide has just passed its peak. Then they begin to drop eggs on the second night following the highest point of the tide, thus assuring that the next cycle of high tides will expose the eggs and allow them to hatch.

The nest-building and tending habits of fresh-water fishes are well known to any fisherman. The nesting habits of the pretty little pumpkinseed fish, a type of fresh-

A Protective Father

The father fertilizes most fish eggs after they have been laid, and often gets the duty of taking care of them too. The male tilapia, a little fish that lives in African rivers and Indonesian ponds, does not take any chances. It scoops up the fertilized eggs from the nest *(right)*, then holds them in its mouth *(below)*. For five days, while the eggs grow, the hungry father fights an urge to close its jaws and swallow. When the young are hatched, it spits them out *(pages 98-99)*.

A Sunfish Grows Up

The young of some fishes, like the ocean sunfish shown, are so different from the adults they are often mistaken for different species. Soon after hatching (*A*), the fish, one eighth of an inch long, develops armor (*B*). In one species, five spikes grow into needles (*C*). Still later the fish changes shape, becoming deeper than it is long (*D*). As an adult (*E*) it may weigh a ton and measure 11 feet in length.

water sunfish, is fairly typical of the group. When spawning time approaches, the male noticeably brightens in color and begins to scoop out a shallow depression in the bottom close to shore. When the nest is ready, he finds a female ready to spawn and escorts her to the nest. Once she has laid her eggs he drives her away and looks for another female. Thus any male's nest may contain the eggs of several females. While the eggs are developing, the male guards the nest against all comers. But his strong protective instinct is often his downfall. If a fishhook drops on his nest he will try to remove it with his mouth and be hooked. A lot of pumpkin-

seeds are caught during the mating season.

The Asiatic family Anabantidae, although not large, includes a number of fish popular with tropical fish hobbyists. The gouramis and the Siamese fighting fish are examples. The male builds a floating nest by producing small bubbles in his mouth. A small amount of mucus goes into the bubbles, making them much stronger than ordinary soap-and-water bubbles. In the wild state, the nests are usually built under some object, such as a leaf, floating on the surface. When enough bubbles have accumulated, courtship of the female follows. The male places her eggs in the nest, guarding and tending

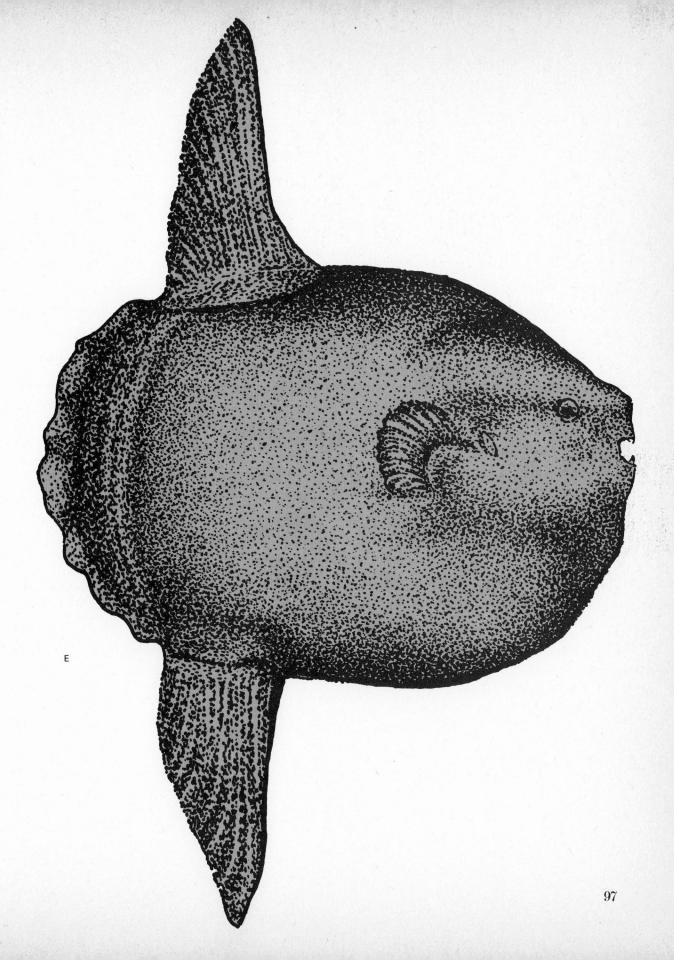

E

them. He is kept very busy since the nest is in constant need of repair. In addition to being beautifully colored, the males have strong protective instincts for their nesting grounds and will protect them against all outsiders. It is for this reason that they have achieved a reputation as fighters.

Perhaps no nesting routine among fishes is more interesting than that of the common stickleback, which lives in the ponds and streams of the Northern Hemisphere. The breeding routine of the sticklebacks begins when the male builds a very fine nest in a quiet-flowing channel among weeds. The nest is tube-shaped and made of bits of stems, roots and other parts of water plants. He holds these together with a sticky fluid from his own kidneys and shapes the nest by rubbing himself against it. The fluid hardens to a cement in the water. He also throws some sand onto the base of the nest to make a sort of foundation. When finished, his home is quite a neat-looking tunnel with a front and back entrance and a clear stream of water flowing through it.

As the courtship starts, the male changes his normal colors to more dramatic ones. He then approaches the female of his choice, driving off rival males with great fury. He leads her to the nest. She lays two or three eggs and then pushes her way out—or is chased out by the male. This is repeated with a number of females until the nest is full of eggs. Then the male stands guard over it for nearly a month, chasing away all other fish, including his former mates. When the young are hatched he takes the nest apart, except for the foundation, which becomes a cradle, and guards the young until they can look out for themselves.

The deep-water anglerfishes also have an unusual breeding habit *(page 88)*. They spend all their lives in dark depths where the chances of boy meeting girl are slim, so the females actually carry their males about with them. Almost as soon as he is hatched a young male fixes himself by his mouth to any part of the female's body. Once he has fastened himself, the tissues of his mouth join with the body of the female. The male remains a dwarf throughout life, fed by his mate's blood stream. Only his reproductive organs are fully developed and function to fertilize the female's eggs, thus assuring the future of the species.

Spitting Out a Family

The male tilapia, which has hatched the eggs of its young in its mouth, sends the baby fish head over tail into their watery world. The tiny fry will use the mouth as a shelter for the next week. But after that, if they should swim into the mouth for protection they may be swallowed by the hungry father.

BUCKING THE CURRENTS of a British Columbia
river, sockeye salmon in their red breeding colors
journey to their spawning grounds. Along the way,
they will face the perils of rapids, manmade dams,
fishermen, hungry bears and birds of prey. The
salmon that make it die exhausted after spawning.

6

The Wondrous Journeys of Fish

Many fishes are constantly on the move. Others, like most of the species that live in coral reefs, have a particular niche or hole to which they retire regularly. Still others, including many that live in fresh water, have well-defined areas or territories, which they patrol and sometimes even guard against all comers. Many, however, follow a general pattern of instinctive seasonal movements. As might be expected, ocean fishes wander great distances, guided by temperatures, currents and supplies of food. Some migrations, however, defy man's ability to explain how they are made.

Migratory behavior is largely seasonal, for many fishes seek out the best spawning grounds and later the best food sources, urged on by changes in temperature and an accompanying change in available food. In winter many fresh-water species stop feeding and go down to deeper levels where temperatures are warmer than on the frozen surface. Some, like the bullhead, settle into the mud for the winter.

On the relatively shallow continental shelves that border the great land masses, there are groups of summer and winter spe-

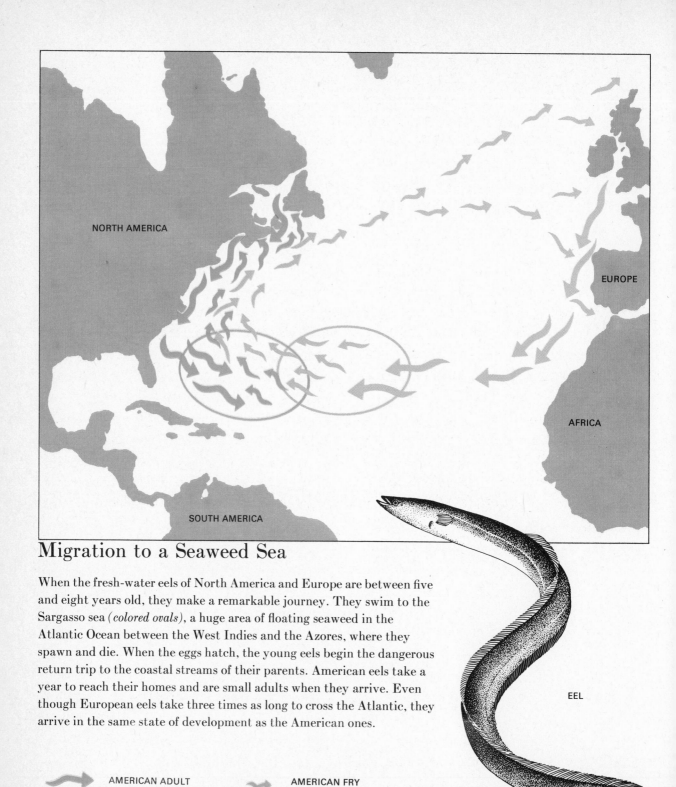

Migration to a Seaweed Sea

When the fresh-water eels of North America and Europe are between five and eight years old, they make a remarkable journey. They swim to the Sargasso sea (*colored ovals*), a huge area of floating seaweed in the Atlantic Ocean between the West Indies and the Azores, where they spawn and die. When the eggs hatch, the young eels begin the dangerous return trip to the coastal streams of their parents. American eels take a year to reach their homes and are small adults when they arrive. Even though European eels take three times as long to cross the Atlantic, they arrive in the same state of development as the American ones.

NORTH AMERICA

EUROPE

AFRICA

SOUTH AMERICA

EEL

AMERICAN ADULT

EUROPEAN ADULT

AMERICAN FRY

EUROPEAN FRY

cies. The summer inshore, or warmer-water species, such as the scup, silver hake and fluke, go out to the edge of the shelf during the winter, where the water temperatures are usually warmer. The winter inshore, or colder-water species, such as the ocean pout and the long-horned sculpin, come close to shore in the winter and go offshore in the summer. Along the eastern coast of the United States the older and bigger fishes of several species drift toward the north.

But the movements of the northern food fishes are quite limited compared with the far-ranging wanderings of the big predatory open-ocean fishes, such as the bluefin and yellowfin tuna and the albacore. Most of these fishes make long journeys north and south, following the summer advance and winter retreat of warm water.

The bluefin tuna is widespread over the North Atlantic, but it is less abundant and smaller in the Pacific. On the American side of the Atlantic it is believed to have a spawning ground in warm subtropical waters somewhere east of the Bahamas. In May and June of each year, schools of bluefin tuna follow the outer side of the Gulf Stream northward in a great parade through the Florida Strait, passing to feeding grounds among the herring and mackerel off Newfoundland and Nova Scotia. The bluefin is never seen returning by this route, however, and how it gets back to its tropical ocean hideout is still a mystery.

In Norway the bluefin is sometimes hunted with harpoons, and harpoons have been recovered from fish caught in the Mediterranean. Two bluefin, tagged in July 1954 off Martha's Vineyard, Massachusetts, were found five years later in the Bay of Biscay, proving that at least some American bluefin do move across to Europe.

Though impressive, these long-distance records made by the bluefin have been broken by its cousin, the albacore. In August 1952, the California Department of Fish and Game tagged 215 albacore just off Los Angeles; nearly 11 months later, one of them was recaptured by a Japanese fishing boat 550 miles southeast of Tokyo. This particular albacore had traveled 4,900 miles in less than a year. In 1956 an albacore was taken 2,670 miles from its release point, and another was caught over 2,000 miles away.

There are many species of fish that move from the sea to fresh water to spawn. The voyages they make range from those of the striped bass and the shad, which live close to shore and move upriver some distance, to those of the salmon, which normally lives as an adult in the sea far from land, but always returns to its birthplace even though it may be in some far inland stream.

It is never safe to generalize about fishes. There are always contradictions, and one of the oddest of these is the case of the landlocked bass that has come to public attention in recent years.

The striped bass, known as the rockfish in the Southern United States, is a migratory

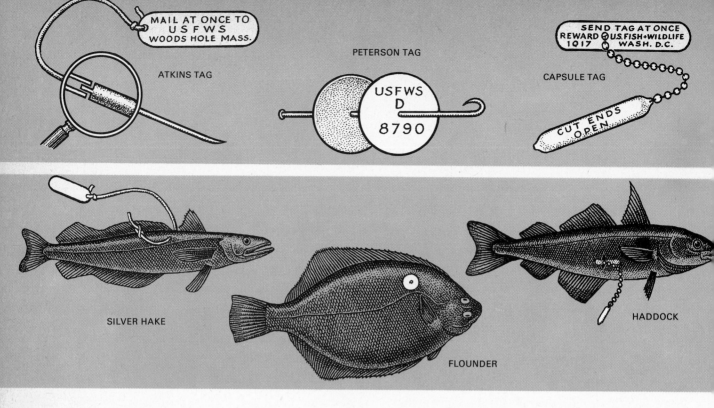

ATKINS TAG

PETERSON TAG

CAPSULE TAG

MAIL AT ONCE TO
USFWS
WOODS HOLE MASS.

SEND TAG AT ONCE
REWARD U.S.FISH+WILDLIFE
1017 WASH. D.C.

CUT ENDS OPEN

USFWS
D
8790

SILVER HAKE

FLOUNDER

HADDOCK

salt-water fish native to the east coast of North America. It normally comes into brackish or fresh water to spawn; after hatching, the young slowly work their way downriver and out to sea again. Striped bass, much sought-after as fine sporting fish, were transplanted 50 years ago with good success into the sea off California. All efforts to plant them in fresh water, however, met with failure—until the Santee-Cooper Hydroelectric Project was completed in 1941.

At that time the bass, which came up the Santee and Cooper Rivers to spawn, found their way back to the sea blocked by two great dams. Behind these dams the river waters backed up to form two sizable bodies of water, Lake Marion and Lake Moultrie. Some bass got through to the sea. But most of the bass were penned up in fresh water— and, oddly enough, they thrived on it. By the late 1950s so many bass were being caught in the lakes that sport fishing had become a multimillion-dollar business.

The migratory instincts of these landlocked striped bass have also become adapted to their new home. Instead of going from the sea up the rivers to spawn, they now go from the lakes higher up the Congaree and Wateree Rivers, and the returning young find all the food they need in the shallow waters of the reservoirs. The adult bass, for their part, have found the gizzard shad, a fresh-water relative of the herring they would be feeding on in the ocean, to be a perfect substitute for their salt-water food.

The Santee-Cooper stripers are a recent example of salt-water fish that have become landlocked, but they are by no means the only ones. On both sides of the North American continent, there are salmon that live in fresh water and never go to sea at all.

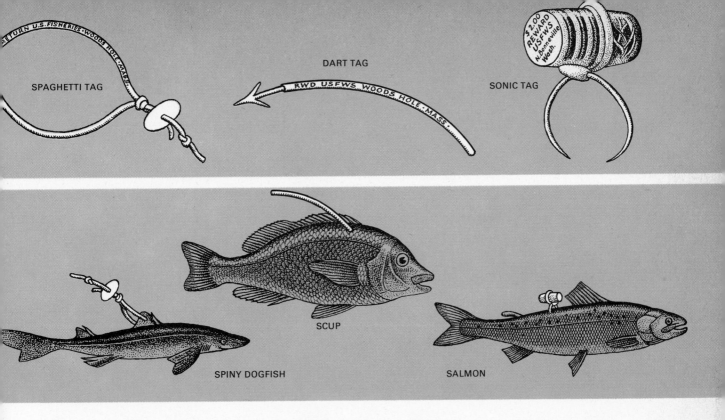

SPAGHETTI TAG

DART TAG

SONIC TAG

SCUP

SPINY DOGFISH

SALMON

Much more typical, however, are the king salmon of the Salmon River in Idaho, which travel out to sea as far north and west as the central Aleutian Islands before returning 2,500 miles to their home spawning grounds. Red, or sockeye, salmon travel more than halfway to Asia from their lakes in British Columbia, and chum salmon from southeast Alaska make many round trips of 3,500 miles to the central Aleutians in search of food.

On the European side of the Atlantic Ocean, salmon have been caught at widely scattered points, and fish tagged in Scotland have been recovered in nets as far away as Greenland, Norway and Iceland. They, too, make ocean voyages of great length. One theory is that they follow the undersea courses of old rivers out across the continental shelves. The Rhine, for example, continues on its ancient bed under the North Sea between the Orkney Islands and Norway.

Many Means of Tagging Fish

To determine their migratory routes, fish are often caught, tagged, and then set free. There are many ways to tag a fish securely without hurting it. The Atkins tag, seen at far left on a silver hake, is a metal label on a wire that is threaded through the back muscles with a needle, which then detaches (as shown under the magnifying glass). The Peterson tag, used for flat-bodied fish, consists of two discs connected through the fish by a pin. The plastic tag seen on the haddock is inserted under the skin; linked to it by a chain is a capsule containing coded information. The "spaghetti" tag is simply a long plastic tube drawn through the dorsal fin and tied to a disc. The flexible "dart" tag is attached by a barbed hook. The newest is the sonic tag, shown hooked to a salmon's back by tiny tongs. In it is a tiny radio transmitter, which helps to track the fish for short distances.

105

There have been many observations and speculations about the manner in which salmon return from the high seas. It has been suggested that they follow currents, or that they guide themselves by the sun using polarized light like bees, or even that they navigate by sighting on the stars and perhaps have a directional memory. None of these suggestions is necessarily foolish, although some border on it. It is unlikely, however, that anything less than an all-out campaign of study will ever answer the fascinating question of how the salmon, in their many millions, find their way from the ocean to the coastal waters near the stream in which they were born.

Once in the coastal waters, the rest of the trip accomplished by the salmon is easier to explain. All rivers, and even streams that

Movement in Masses

Some 4,000 species of fish travel in schools, which
help protect them by giving an enemy the difficult
problem of attacking a large mass of individuals.
At left, a formation of tuna knifes through the waters
of the Gulf Stream near the Bahama Islands. Sweeping
northward, the fish may appear off Long Island in the
summer, off Nova Scotia in the fall. Below, a vast
school of herring, packed solidly, swims through
the clear waters off the Virgin Islands.

feed into them, are believed to have their own odor that the fish can recognize, although the distinctive smell may be very weak. In one study, for example, salmon were captured upstream and returned to the river below where their native streams joined. Some of the fish had their noses plugged. These fish were unable to find their way back to their native stream, while those with unplugged nostrils were able to do so quite easily.

If a salmon finds its native river blocked, it may go up a neighboring one and start a new spawning run as a result. Many of our rivers nowadays have become effectively blocked to spawning runs of salmon by both dams and pollution. However, it takes quite a lot to stop a salmon on its way to its spawning ground. Salmon going upstream are said to travel at a speed of six or seven miles per hour, and the habit that both salmon and trout have of leaping up waterfalls is well known and most spectacular. They leap heights of 8 to 10 feet at a clip. If they do not succeed at first, they go on trying until they either succeed or fall back exhausted.

Salmon traveling to spawn do not feed, and become steadily thinner and weaker. Indeed the king, or Chinook, salmon, on its journey to its spawning ground thousands of miles up the Yukon, may fail for this reason and die before it completes the journey. As every fisherman knows, Atlantic salmon running upstream will snap at flies, but this may be a mere feeding reflex; it has been suggested that salmon go for flies that look most like the creatures they eat in the sea.

What urge makes salmon travel upstream, leaping waterfalls and exposing themselves to many dangers, only to die when spawning is done? It may be that they are returning to ancestral spawning grounds. It is possible that ages ago their permanent home was in fresh water. The salmon's ancestors may have simply migrated out to sea on a feeding journey, remained to live but returned to fresh water to spawn.

Some fishes reverse the life history of the salmon, spending their youth in fresh water but traveling out to sea to spawn. The best known is the common eel. Others include some small fish of the Southern Hemisphere called smelts in the Falkland Islands and, when young, whitebait in New Zealand, which run down the streams and spawn in schools in the surf.

The tracking-down of the spawning area of the fresh-water eel is one of the great stories of marine biology. Until the end of the 18th Century no one had ever seen eels bear young, so it had been supposed that eels simply came out of the mud. Then, in the 19th Century, it was noted in Italy that adult eels went down to the sea and young ones came up out of it into fresh water. In 1856 a German scientist described a flat, transparent creature that he had caught in the Strait of Messina, between Sicily and Italy. He did not recognize it as having anything to do with eels and named it *Lepto-*

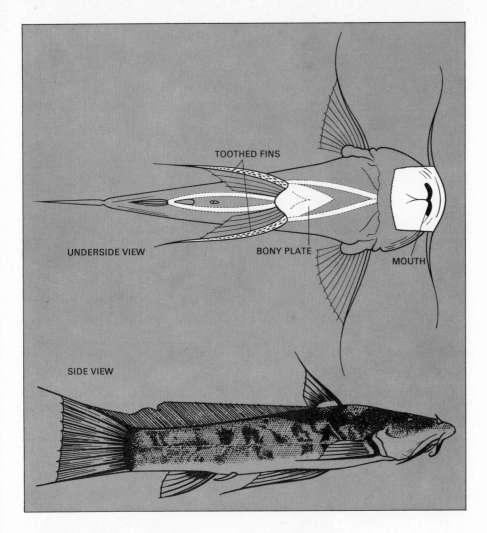

TOOTHED FINS

UNDERSIDE VIEW

BONY PLATE

MOUTH

SIDE VIEW

A Fish That Walks Up Walls

Although a clumsy swimmer, this South American
catfish can climb the stone face of a waterfall. First it
clamps onto the rock surface with its "sucker" mouth.
Then it uses powerful muscles, attached to a bony
plate in its belly, to move its lower fins forward. These
fins are equipped with tiny, sharp, backward-pointing
teeth, which grip the rock surface so that the fish
can move its mouth farther up. In this way the fish
can hitch itself up a 20-foot rock wall in half an hour.

cephalus brevirostris (short-snouted thin-head). In 1896 two Italian scientists discovered that this was the larva of the eel. They too worked in the Strait of Messina, where the tide casts up plankton in masses on the shore. By examining hundreds of stranded leptocephali the Italian scientists were able to establish beyond doubt that the larvae were related to the grown eel.

At the beginning of the 20th Century, Danish research ships in the North Atlantic found leptocephalus eggs by the hundreds in the open ocean. A young Danish marine biologist, Johannes Schmidt, began an intensive search with fine-meshed nets towed by Danish ships at various depths all over the North Atlantic Ocean. He searched through hundreds of hauls and found that he could draw up a chart showing that the leptocephali became smaller and smaller in size as one approached the Sargasso Sea, a calm seaweedy area northeast of the West Indies. It was in this sea that the smallest eggs of all were found.

The conclusion Schmidt drew from this was that the European and American fresh-water eels spawned in the Sargasso Sea in depths of about 1,200 feet. (Further study has shown that the American eel has a spawning area to the west of that of the European eel, nearer to the American coast.)

Leptocephali hatch in the spring and drift northward with the Gulf Stream. The American type has a shorter youth than the European type, and arrives the following winter on the east coast of the United States. The European eggs drift far north in the Gulf Stream. It takes them about three years to drift to the coast of Europe.

In the spring following their arrival off both coasts, the leptocephali lose their flattened, ribbonlike shape and become "glass" eels about three inches long. They then migrate upriver to distant ponds and streams, sometimes in enormous swarms. In the Severn River in England these swarms are known as "eelfares," and the eels are caught in nets in vast quantities.

In late summer and early fall, the eels leave their rivers and ponds and make their way downstream to the sea. Their color changes from a yellowish sheen to silver, and they begin the long journey to the Sargasso Sea. Like the salmon, the silver eel will not feed at all during its difficult but vital migration to its far-off spawning ground.

When Salmon Run, Bears Feast

An enemy from the forest, this big brown bear seizes
a chum salmon from the McNeil River in Alaska.
When the salmon swim upstream to spawn in June
and July, brown bears feed almost entirely on the fish.
Gulls, like the one at right, stand by waiting for scraps.
Other birds of prey dive down on the salmon remains.

111

LEAVING THEIR SCHOONER, Portuguese cod
fishermen set out at dawn in one-man dories for a
lonely day's fishing on the Grand Banks of
Newfoundland where they use old-fashioned hand
lines. Today 15 nations, many with modern equipment,
compete for the rich harvest of cod on the Banks.

7

Harvesting Food from the Sea

In 1883 Thomas Henry Huxley, the eminent English biologist and writer, summed up a belief man has had for centuries: "Probably all the great sea-fisheries are inexhaustible; that is to say, that nothing we do seriously affects the numbers of fish." Today, however, Huxley's confident words have a slightly hollow ring. Man has at last begun to realize that the sea, for all its seeming

113

Where Fish Are Caught

The best places to catch large quantities of fish are along the sloping shelves of the continents. Here, plant and animal plankton thrive, providing schools of fish with plentiful supplies of food. The coasts of Europe, North America and east Asia are heavily fished, but many countries in Africa, South America and west Asia lack the large, efficient fishing fleets needed to harvest their rich waters. If these fleets could be developed, they would help in lessening the food shortages found today in those continents.

HEAVILY FISHED AREAS

MODERATELY FISHED AREAS

POTENTIAL FISHING AREAS

plenty, has its limits as a source of food.

Men have fished for as long as they have hunted, and that is a long time. They have always taken the resources of the waters for granted, and as populations grew and nations became industrial, men have expanded their fisheries to keep up with the increased demand. For fish is one of the staple foods, one of the richest of all sources of animal protein. In a world faced with a population explosion it may be essential to mankind's continued survival.

The amount of fish taken from the world's waters has been rising constantly and today totals more than 55 million tons a year. Some 35 per cent of this total is eaten fresh; the rest is cured, canned, frozen, made into an edible powder called fish meal, or turned into agricultural fertilizer. About 85 per cent of the total, or some 48 million tons of fish, comes from the sea; the rest is hooked or netted in rivers and lakes.

Yet fish and other kinds of sea food still account for only a small fraction of the world's total supply of protein. Thus the demand for fish is bound to result in even bigger catches. At the same time, man has only just begun serious study of how to safeguard the available supply, and if possible increase it.

Five countries contribute well over half of the world's total harvest of sea and fresh-water fish. Japan was for a long time the leading fishing nation, but her recent catches of nearly seven million tons a year are now far surpassed by those of Peru. Blessed with swarms of anchoveta just off her coast, Peru

ASIA

NORTH AMERICA

EUROPE

ASIA

Pacific Ocean

Atlantic Ocean

AFRICA

SOUTH AMERICA

AUSTRALIA

takes in nearly 10 million tons annually. There are no recent estimates available, but judging by old figures, Communist China undoubtedly belongs among the top three. Soviet Russia is ranked fourth, with an annual catch of some five million tons, and the United States is fifth. Norway, Spain, India, Canada and Iceland are the next most important fishing countries, each contributing more than a million tons to the world's annual supply.

Most of the world's fisheries lie in the off-shore waters of the continents in depths of less than 1,200 feet. All these continental shelves combined occupy only about 10 per cent of the area of the oceans, but the amount of fish they produce is huge. For these are the regions where conditions are most suitable for abundance of sea life. This is where the plankton thrive, as do the many plants and creatures of the bottom that provide the food for vast numbers of bottom-dwelling and open-ocean fishes. And here, just off shore, the fishing nations of the world are engaged in a sharp competition to reap the riches of the sea, a struggle that is filled with peril for the food-fish population as a whole.

The tools employed to harvest the sea are of many different types, and in recent years their efficiency has increased to an alarming degree. Fifty years ago fishing fleets consisted mainly of single vessels going out with trawls or purse seines and dories from which were trailed long lines of baited hooks. Today, fleets are more like huge naval task forces, complete with mother ships, spotters,

Nets for All Occasions

Shown here are some of the many home-made fishing nets and traps developed by Africans. Men on platforms over the swift-running Congo River lower cone-shaped baskets into which the current sweeps the fish. Fishermen in shallow waters clap a hand-hole basket over the fish and pull them through the top. Women in Uganda use large basket-nets to drive fish into a small area where they can be scooped up and placed in containers. Another device is the basket trap, which is anchored with bait placed inside. Fish swim in after the bait, then cannot find their way out.

catchers, and floating factories for immediate processing of the fish caught. The basic catching tool is still the otter trawl, a great, wide-mouthed net towed along the sea bottom or in the middle depths. But it is used with far greater efficiency than ever before.

Planes are sent out to find schools of fish, and electronic echo sounders can be so delicately adjusted that they can even locate fish lying on the bottom. Soon to come are television cameras towed underwater to enable the fishermen on the surface to spot fish. These cameras will feed information to equally amazing equipment—electronic computers that will steer the trawling nets and adjust their depths to the most effective level for catching particular kinds of fish.

How serious is the actual threat to the world's fish supply? As yet, we have only

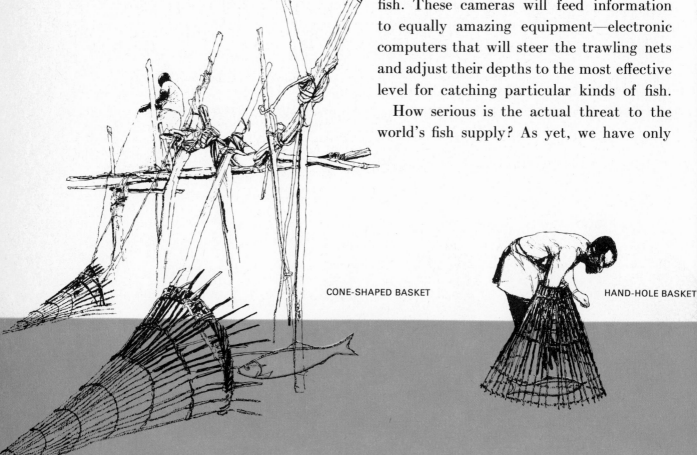

CONE-SHAPED BASKET

HAND-HOLE BASKET

some general indications. We know that the trawlers of many nations have been forced to go farther and farther afield to find the larger catches needed to make their expensive equipment profitable. The Japanese now fish in every ocean; Russian trawlers by the score fish the banks between Cape Cod and Nova Scotia and are pushing ever deeper into the Bering Sea on the other side of North America.

Unquestionably, some of the big traditional fishing grounds are in danger of being overfished. But other areas, notably the territorial waters around some of the less advanced nations, could support far heavier commercial fishing. And here may lie the key to increasing the world's total food-fish supply. Often, improved catches require only somewhat better equipment and some advice from experienced fishermen, as one

recent example from Ecuador clearly shows.

There are more than 100 small fishing villages along the coast of Ecuador, serving as home ports for some 10,000 fishermen. Although the area has a few modern plants for processing and exporting shrimp and tuna, the fishing itself is done with methods and equipment hundreds of years old. Three main types of boat are used: balsa rafts rigged with sails, dugout canoes cut from cedar logs and planked sailboats up to 35 feet long. Most nets are handmade from cotton fibers; the durable nylon netting now used in modern fisheries around the world is too expensive for this area.

In February 1950, the United Nations' Food and Agriculture Organization (FAO) sent a young American master fisherman named Erling Oswald to these coastal villages. He brought with him one small diesel

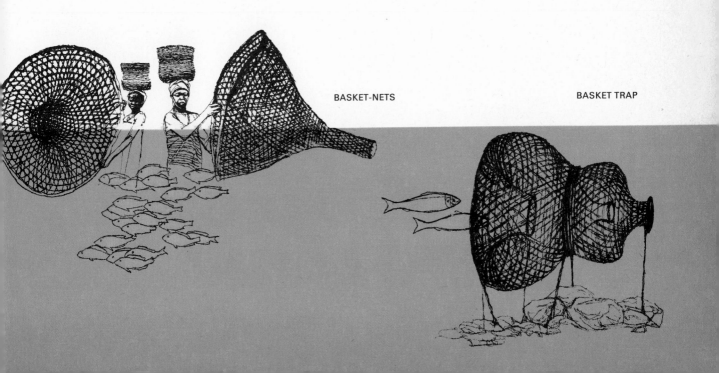

BASKET-NETS   BASKET TRAP

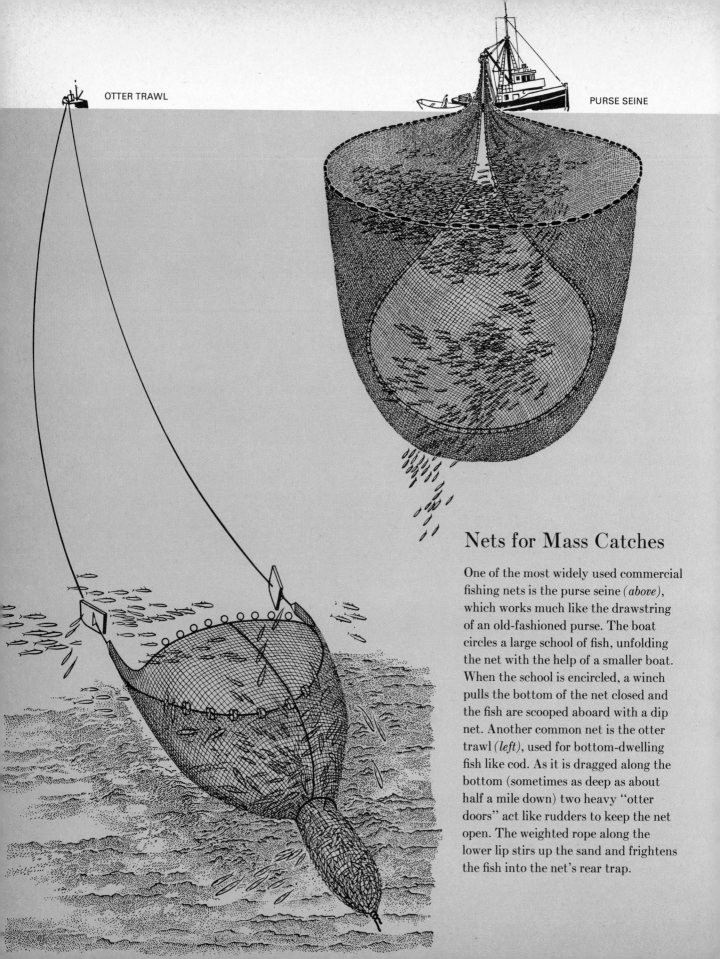

Nets for Mass Catches

One of the most widely used commercial fishing nets is the purse seine (*above*), which works much like the drawstring of an old-fashioned purse. The boat circles a large school of fish, unfolding the net with the help of a smaller boat. When the school is encircled, a winch pulls the bottom of the net closed and the fish are scooped aboard with a dip net. Another common net is the otter trawl (*left*), used for bottom-dwelling fish like cod. As it is dragged along the bottom (sometimes as deep as about half a mile down) two heavy "otter doors" act like rudders to keep the net open. The weighted rope along the lower lip stirs up the sand and frightens the fish into the net's rear trap.

engine and an assortment of nylon nets and lines, fishing lures, mechanical and hand winches and fishing lamps, all provided by the FAO. The Ecuadorian government supplied Oswald with a 23-foot sailboat. He installed the engine in the sailboat, hired a crew and went to work.

The result, to the Ecuadorians, was startling. With his one small, engine-driven boat and modern equipment, Oswald brought in more than half a ton of tuna daily—almost as much as the total daily catch made by all the canoes and sailboats used by the fishermen of the town of Manta, where he began his demonstrations.

Oswald demonstrated the greatly improved fishing techniques made possible by modern equipment. But even more important he demonstrated that this equipment, once put to use, quickly paid for itself. In two years all of the costs of his own boat were paid for by the fish he caught, and he had started a small revolution among these Ecuadorian fishermen who for so long had been unable to improve on the old ways.

With the help of the U.S. International Cooperation Administration and the Ecuadorian Ministry of Social Welfare, $6,000 was provided for the purchase of several small diesel engines. Denmark sent a marine engineer to help install them and to train the fishermen in their operation and upkeep. The fishermen, in turn, adapted their boats at their own expense. The FAO lent them efficient nylon gill nets. Thus equipped, one

25-foot boat from Santa Rosa brought in almost 34,000 pounds of pompano, spadefish, sierra and tuna in its first 14 days of operations—despite the fact that the best part of the fishing season was over for that year. The original loan of $6,000 was paid off shortly, and the fishermen got additional funds of $10,000, six more diesel engines and more than 2,000 pounds of nylon webbing and twine. So encouraging were the results that the Ecuadorian government itself embarked on a four-year, $633,000 program to broaden Oswald's work. As the result of one man's efforts the days of the balsa raft and the dugout canoe along Ecuador's coast are already numbered.

Ecuador is an example of how, in some areas of the world, fishing efficiency can be increased and more fish taken without any danger of overfishing. The same techniques could be very profitably applied in many parts of Africa and Asia such as the Arabian Sea and the southern waters of Australia.

A startling contrast to such expanding activities is the extraordinary decline of one of the great fishing powers of the world—the United States. There are three causes for this decline: the old-fashioned methods used by many American fishermen; the high cost of building new fishing equipment in this country; and a law, passed in 1792 and still on the books, which forbids American fishermen to land catches in any but American-built boats. Today this country's share of

(*Text continued on page 123*)

Portuguese fishermen labor to launch a colorful but cumbersome boat;

the prize they seek is the sardines that swarm beyond the pounding surf.

Exploring the Ocean Deep

Divers inspect the complicated gear beneath a modern
submarine-research vessel. With such ships, scientists
can study undersea currents and gather samples of
fish and plankton. In this way they can find out more
about how fishes live, where they travel and what
they eat, and possibly learn how to restock the sea.

the world fishery production is down to 5.2 per cent, from 13 per cent in 1948.

Fishery research in the United States is as good as any in the world, but in its resources it lags considerably behind such leading competitors as the Soviet Union and Japan. Much of the technological equipment of the United States fishing fleet is out of date. While the other leading fishing nations send out fleets equipped to process fish on the high seas, many American fishermen must still bring their catch back to port before it can be handled. The combined fleets of the once-great ports of Boston and Gloucester numbered 500 boats at the end of World War II. But their largest vessel is smaller than the smallest boat in the Soviet fleet of 150 modern craft that in recent years has been in almost constant operation on the rich fishing areas off Cape Cod.

Another way to increase the world supply of vital protein foods that fish can supply is through better use of fish that are caught. One of the most promising methods of doing this lies in the manufacture of fish meal and fish flour, products made by processing fish into dry, powdery form. These make full use of the parts of commercial food-fish normally disposed of as garbage. They also make use of what fishermen call "trash-fish" —skates, dogfish, searobins and others that often make up half the catch of a trawler and are ordinarily thrown away.

Norway began research on fish meal for human consumption as far back as the late 1880s, and since then a great many advances have been made. Peru produces hundreds of thousands of tons of fish meal annually. Fish protein concentrate (FPC), a recent development in the United States, is produced by turning the entire fish—scales, intestines and all—into a colorless, odorless, chemically pure white powder. This powder, rich in animal proteins, can be used in a variety of ways—in stews, vegetable dishes or mixed with wheat flour. Best of all, FPC is so cheap to manufacture it could meet the animal protein needs of all people in the world at a cost of only half a cent per person a day.

Yet the question still remains—will the world population of fish be able to resist the steady increase in man's power to catch fish? Will we ever be able to replenish or increase that supply by cultivating fish in our waters as efficiently as farmers cultivate their crops on land?

In fresh water, fish cultivation is an old story—and one that can profitably be brought up to date. In Europe carp have been cultivated since the Middle Ages, a time when every monastery and many a feudal lord's castle had its own carp pond. Fish have been raised for centuries in ponds and rice paddies in the Orient. Even today, mainland China gets almost half of its annual catch of fish from fresh-water sources inland. Raising fish in rice paddies actually improves the rice crop, since the fish feed on insect, plant and animal pests that attack and damage the growing rice.

Fresh-water fishes lend themselves to cultivation, and represent a hope for the future in the world's food supply. But how can man ever cultivate the vastness of the sea?

Some promising beginnings—and some startling proposals—have been made. Shortly after World War II experiments were carried out to speed up fish growth in several Scottish lochs, long, narrow bays partially open to the sea. The lochs were fertilized with chemicals in the spring and early summer. The immediate result was a great increase in animal and plant plankton. Fish called plaice were then introduced into the lochs to thrive on the rich food supply. Not only did they thrive, but they actually added two years' growth in six months' time.

Despite these and other interesting experiments, man's best hope right now seems to lie in exercising some control over the amount of fish caught in the heavily used fisheries of the continental shelves. At the same time man must begin to use new areas whose fish can still be harvested without endangering the total fish population.

Now is the time to heed the warning. The whaling industry has advanced to the point where the number of whales is so reduced and the expeditions themselves are so expensive to equip and send out that few are still profitable. How long will it be before that point is reached in other fisheries?

To control fishing activities—and add more fish to the sea as present stocks are reduced—we must know more about the fishes themselves. We need more detailed information about the natural history of fishes, their feeding and breeding habits, their growth, their migrations and all aspects of the watery world in which they live. For nearly half a century each major nation of the world has had its own organization for carrying out this kind of research, in waters used by its own fishermen.

More recently, working through international organizations, these nations have increased their efforts to share the knowledge they have gained. These international programs may help to solve the urgent problem of feeding all the hungry peoples of the world. And in doing so, they may also encourage the broader cooperation and understanding among nations that is the major necessity facing mankind today.

Treasure in a Basket

Basket boats on a lake in southern India are typical of the primitive fishing equipment used in many parts of the world. In these areas, meat is so scarce that for millions of people fish is the only source of vital animal protein. Unless fish harvesting is improved, many will have to go without this protein entirely.

Index

Numerals in italics indicate a photograph or painting of the subject mentioned.

Credits

The sources for the illustrations in this book are shown below. Credits for pictures from left to right are separated by commas, top to bottom by dashes.

Cover—Tom Hutchins
Contents—René Martin—Margaret L. Estey—Martha Alexander—Rudolf Freund—Martha Alexander—René Martin—Anthony Saris
6—George Silk
8—René Martin
11-17—Rudolf Freund
18, 19—Enid Kotschnig
20, 21—Margaret L. Estey
22-25—René Martin
27—John Dominis
28—J. R. Eyerman
30-33—Jack J. Kunz
34-38—Margaret L. Estey
41—Margaret L. Estey
42—Michael Rougier
44-45—Matt Greene
47—Fritz Goro
48-49—Henry G. Young
50-51—Martha Alexander
52, 53—Ernest L. Libby at Marine Studios Marineland Fla., Fritz Goro
54-55—Martha Alexander
56, 57—Jack J. Kunz
58, 59—Coles Phinizy, Margaret L. Estey
60-61—Jack Fields
62-63—Peter Gimbel
65—Peter Gimbel
66—Carroll Seghers II from Black Star
68-69—Margaret L. Estey
70, 71—Harry Pederson
72, 73—George Skadding
74-75—Gaetano Di Palma
76, 77—Martha Alexander
78, 79—Ernest L. Libby, Ron Church—John G. New
80—Rudolf Freund
82, 83—Ron Church, Rudolf Freund
84, 85—N. R. Farbman
86—Douglas Wilson
88, 89—Rudolf Freund, Martha Alexander, Martha Alexander
90, 91—Margaret L. Estey, Margaret L. Estey, Martha Alexander
92—Martha Alexander
95—Wallace Kirkland
96, 97—Margaret L. Estey
99—Wallace Kirkland
100—Don LeBlanc from Annan Photo Service
102—Matt Greene and Martha Alexander
104-105—René Martin
106, 107—Fritz Goro—Elgin T. Ciampi
109—Stephen Chan
111—Fritz Goro
112-113—Leonard McCombe
114-115—Matt Greene
116-117—Anthony Saris
118—Matt Greene
120-121—Eliot Elisofon
122—Dr. Robert F. Dill
125—Howard Sochurek
End papers—Otto von Eersel

For Further Reading

Axelrod, Herbert R., *Color Guide to Tropical Fish.* Sterling, 1959
Axelrod, Herbert R. and Leonard P. Schultz, *Handbook of Tropical Aquarium Fishes.* McGraw, 1955
Bendick, Jeanne, *First Book of Fishes.* Watts, 1965
Buehr, Walter, *Harvest of the Sea.* Morrow, 1955
Burger, Carl, *All About Fish.* Random House, 1960
Carson, Rachel, *Under The Sea Wind.* Oxford University Press, 1952
Coggins, Jack, *Nets Overboard!* Dodd, 1965
Fichter, George S., *Fishes.* Golden Press, 1963
Gilbert, Miriam, *Starting an Aquarium.* Hammond, 1961
Harrison, C. William., *First Book of Commercial Fishing.* Watts, 1964
Hess, Lilo, *Sea Horses.* Scribner's, 1966
Hofsinde, Robert, *Indian Fishing and Camping.* Morrow, 1963
National Geographic Society, ed. John Oliver La Gorce, *Book of Fishes.* The Society, 1958
Ommanney, F. D. and the Editors of TIME-LIFE BOOKS, *The Fishes.* Time Inc., 1963
Place, Marion T., *Let's Go to a Fish Hatchery.* Putnam, 1967
Selsam, Millicent E., *Underwater Zoos.* Morrow, 1961
Shapp, Martha and Charles, *Let's Find Out About Fishes.* Watts, 1965
Straughan, Robert P.L., *Sharks, Morays and Treasures.* Barnes and Noble, 1965
Sutton, Felix, *How and Why Wonder Book of Fish.* Grosset, 1963
Valens, Evans G., *Wingfin and Topple.* World Publishing Co., 1962
Zim, Herbert S., *Fish.* Golden Press, 1959
Fishes, A Guide to Fresh- and Salt-Water Species. Golden Press, 1956
Sharks. Morrow, 1966

Acknowledgments

The editors are indebted to the staff of the LIFE Nature Library, from which this volume is adapted; the staff for this edition: Stanley Fillmore, editor; Eric Gluckman, designer; John von Hartz, writer; Eleanor Feltser, Susan Marcus and Theo Pascal, researchers; David L. Harrison and Madge Raymond, copyreaders; Virginia Wells, art assistant.